Building *the* Best YOU

A TWO-YEAR
DISCOVERY
JOURNAL

Caroline Harper

STERLING
New York

STERLING
New York

An Imprint of Sterling Publishing
387 Park Avenue South
New York, NY 10016

ISBN 978-1-4351-4915-1

Distributed in Canada by Sterling Publishing
c/o Canadian Manda Group, 165 Dufferin Street
Toronto, Ontario, Canada M6K 3H6
Distributed in the United Kingdom by GMC Distribution Services
Castle Place, 166 High Street, Lewes, East Sussex, England BN7 1XU
Distributed in Australia by Capricorn Link (Australia) Pty. Ltd.
P.O. Box 704, Windsor, NSW 2756, Australia

For information about custom editions, special sales, and premium
and corporate purchases, please contact Sterling Special Sales
at 800-805-5489 or specialsales@sterlingpublishing.com.

Manufactured in China

4   6   8   10   9   7   5   3

www.sterlingpublishing.com

INTRODUCTION

B uilding the best YOU there is, and checking in with where you are daily, is the promise. Reclaim your identity and make yourself into the person you have always admired—the person you strive to be. With these basic questions and five minutes of "focus time" a day, you can get there. Not only will you see results from year to year with this two-year journal—you will see a difference from day to day.

Chart your entries and notice patterns. For the first year, fill in the column on the left side of each page. For the second, fill in the column on the right. About every six weeks, you will arrive at a larger set of questions which will prompt you to further reflect on the days past. These questions are spread over two pages and appear twice; fill in the first two pages during the first year, and the second two pages during the second year.

Building the Best YOU doesn't attack and bemoan all that is negative. It helps you highlight the courage, joy, hope, forgiveness, and love that live inside. This journal helps you mine these treasures that are so often out of reach.

Build the things that make a *life worth living* your priority. Notice the negative things you say to yourself. Try an exercise: pretend the negatives were said by someone "whose mission in life was to make [you] miserable," and then fight back. That way, says Martin Seligman, "you don't blindly accept your own insults."

Nurture your strengths, not your negativity.

Nurture human virtues: Satisfaction, Contentment, Fulfillment, Pride, Serenity.

Ask yourself "What's right?" and live your life around those strengths. After inviting this self-discovery process into your life, you will begin to appreciate the little things that you bring to bear and you will build on those strengths. Ultimately those virtues—which are located within but have been brought out on these pages—will spell out the mystical meaning and purpose you have been seeking. You will have built the best YOU there is.

What did I do today? _____

_____

_____

_____

_____

What did I feel today? _____

_____

_____

_____

_____

What am I grateful for today? _____

_____

_____

_____

_____

What challenged me today? _____

_____

_____

_____

_____

How can I overcome that challenge? _____

_____

_____

_____

_____

What did I savor today? _____

_____

_____

_____

_____

YEAR ONE

Date

What did I do today? _____

_____

_____

_____

_____

What did I feel today? _____

_____

_____

_____

_____

What am I grateful for today? _____

_____

_____

_____

_____

What challenged me today? _____

_____

_____

_____

_____

How can I overcome that challenge? _____

_____

_____

_____

_____

What did I savor today? _____

_____

_____

_____

_____

YEAR TWO

BUILDING *the* BEST YOU THERE IS

_____ Date

What did I do today? _____
_____
_____
_____

What did I feel today? _____
_____
_____
_____

What am I grateful for today? _____
_____
_____
_____

What challenged me today? _____
_____
_____
_____

How can I overcome that challenge? _____
_____
_____
_____

What did I savor today? _____
_____
_____
_____

_____ Date

What did I do today? _____
_____
_____
_____

What did I feel today? _____
_____
_____
_____

What am I grateful for today? _____
_____
_____
_____

What challenged me today? _____
_____
_____
_____

How can I overcome that challenge? _____
_____
_____
_____

What did I savor today? _____
_____
_____
_____

YEAR ONE

YEAR TWO

BUILDING _the_ BEST YOU THERE IS

_____ Date   _____ Date

What did I do today? _____   *What did I do today?* _____
_____   _____
_____   _____
_____   _____
_____   _____

What did I feel today? _____   *What did I feel today?* _____
_____   _____
_____   _____
_____   _____
_____   _____

What am I grateful for today? _____   *What am I grateful for today?* _____
_____   _____
_____   _____
_____   _____
_____   _____

What challenged me today? _____   *What challenged me today?* _____
_____   _____
_____   _____
_____   _____
_____   _____

How can I overcome that challenge? _____   *How can I overcome that challenge?* _____
_____   _____
_____   _____
_____   _____
_____   _____

What did I savor today? _____   *What did I savor today?* _____
_____   _____
_____   _____
_____   _____
_____   _____

YEAR ONE   YEAR TWO

BUILDING *the* BEST YOU THERE IS

What did I do today? _____

_____
_____
_____
_____

What did I feel today? _____

_____
_____
_____
_____

What am I grateful for today? _____

_____
_____
_____

What challenged me today? _____

_____
_____
_____
_____

How can I overcome that challenge? _____

_____
_____
_____
_____

What did I savor today? _____

_____
_____
_____

What did I do today? _____

_____
_____
_____
_____

What did I feel today? _____

_____
_____
_____
_____

What am I grateful for today? _____

_____
_____
_____

What challenged me today? _____

_____
_____
_____
_____

How can I overcome that challenge? _____

_____
_____
_____
_____

What did I savor today? _____

_____
_____
_____

BUILDING the BEST YOU THERE IS

_____ Date

What did I do today? _____
_____
_____
_____
_____

What did I feel today? _____
_____
_____
_____
_____

What am I grateful for today? _____
_____
_____
_____
_____

What challenged me today? _____
_____
_____
_____
_____

How can I overcome that challenge? _____
_____
_____
_____
_____

What did I savor today? _____
_____
_____
_____
_____

_____ Date

What did I do today? _____
_____
_____
_____
_____

What did I feel today? _____
_____
_____
_____
_____

What am I grateful for today? _____
_____
_____
_____
_____

What challenged me today? _____
_____
_____
_____
_____

How can I overcome that challenge? _____
_____
_____
_____
_____

What did I savor today? _____
_____
_____
_____
_____

YEAR ONE

YEAR TWO

BUILDING *the* BEST YOU THERE IS

What did I do today? _____

_____

_____

_____

What did I feel today? _____

_____

_____

_____

What am I grateful for today? _____

_____

_____

_____

What challenged me today? _____

_____

_____

_____

How can I overcome that challenge? _____

_____

_____

_____

What did I savor today? _____

_____

_____

_____

What did I do today? _____

_____

_____

_____

What did I feel today? _____

_____

_____

_____

What am I grateful for today? _____

_____

_____

_____

What challenged me today? _____

_____

_____

_____

How can I overcome that challenge? _____

_____

_____

_____

What did I savor today? _____

_____

_____

_____

BUILDING *the* BEST YOU THERE IS

_____ Date

What did I do today? _____
_____
_____
_____
_____

What did I feel today? _____
_____
_____
_____
_____

What am I grateful for today? _____
_____
_____
_____
_____

What challenged me today? _____
_____
_____
_____
_____

How can I overcome that challenge? ____
_____
_____
_____
_____

What did I savor today? _____
_____
_____
_____
_____

YEAR ONE

_____ Date

What did I do today? _____
_____
_____
_____
_____

What did I feel today? _____
_____
_____
_____
_____

What am I grateful for today? _____
_____
_____
_____
_____

What challenged me today? _____
_____
_____
_____
_____

How can I overcome that challenge? ____
_____
_____
_____
_____

What did I savor today? _____
_____
_____
_____
_____

YEAR TWO

BUILDING _the_ BEST YOU THERE IS

_____ Date

What did I do today? _____
_____
_____
_____
_____

What did I feel today? _____
_____
_____
_____
_____

What am I grateful for today? _____
_____
_____
_____
_____

What challenged me today? _____
_____
_____
_____

How can I overcome that challenge? _____
_____
_____
_____
_____

What did I savor today? _____
_____
_____
_____
_____

YEAR ONE

_____ Date

What did I do today? _____
_____
_____
_____
_____

What did I feel today? _____
_____
_____
_____
_____

What am I grateful for today? _____
_____
_____
_____
_____

What challenged me today? _____
_____
_____
_____

How can I overcome that challenge? _____
_____
_____
_____
_____

What did I savor today? _____
_____
_____
_____
_____

YEAR TWO

BUILDING _the_ BEST YOU THERE IS

What did I do today? _____

What did I do today? _____

_____

_____

_____

_____

_____

_____

_____

_____

What did I feel today? _____

What did I feel today? _____

_____

_____

_____

_____

_____

_____

_____

_____

What am I grateful for today? _____

What am I grateful for today? _____

_____

_____

_____

_____

_____

_____

_____

_____

What challenged me today? _____

What challenged me today? _____

_____

_____

_____

_____

_____

_____

_____

_____

How can I overcome that challenge? _____

How can I overcome that challenge? _____

_____

_____

_____

_____

_____

_____

_____

_____

What did I savor today? _____

What did I savor today? _____

_____

_____

_____

_____

_____

_____

YEAR ONE

YEAR TWO

BUILDING *the* BEST YOU THERE IS

Date _____

What did I do today? _____
_____
_____
_____
_____

What did I feel today? _____
_____
_____
_____
_____

What am I grateful for today? _____
_____
_____
_____
_____

What challenged me today? _____
_____
_____
_____

How can I overcome that challenge? _____
_____
_____
_____

What did I savor today? _____
_____
_____
_____

YEAR ONE

Date _____

What did I do today? _____
_____
_____
_____
_____

What did I feel today? _____
_____
_____
_____
_____

What am I grateful for today? _____
_____
_____
_____
_____

What challenged me today? _____
_____
_____
_____

How can I overcome that challenge? _____
_____
_____
_____

What did I savor today? _____
_____
_____
_____

YEAR TWO

BUILDING the BEST YOU THERE IS

_____ Date

What did I do today? _____

_____
_____
_____

What did I feel today? _____

_____
_____
_____

What am I grateful for today? _____

_____
_____
_____

What challenged me today? _____

_____
_____
_____

How can I overcome that challenge? ____

_____
_____
_____

What did I savor today? _____

_____
_____
_____

YEAR ONE

_____ Date

What did I do today? _____

_____
_____
_____

What did I feel today? _____

_____
_____
_____

What am I grateful for today? _____

_____
_____
_____

What challenged me today? _____

_____
_____
_____

How can I overcome that challenge? ____

_____
_____
_____

What did I savor today? _____

_____
_____
_____

YEAR TWO

_____ Date

What did I do today? _____

_____
_____
_____
_____

What did I feel today? _____

_____
_____
_____
_____

What am I grateful for today? _____

_____
_____
_____
_____

What challenged me today? _____

_____
_____
_____
_____

How can I overcome that challenge? _____

_____
_____
_____
_____

What did I savor today? _____

_____
_____
_____
_____

YEAR ONE

_____ Date

What did I do today? _____

_____
_____
_____
_____

What did I feel today? _____

_____
_____
_____
_____

What am I grateful for today? _____

_____
_____
_____
_____

What challenged me today? _____

_____
_____
_____
_____

How can I overcome that challenge? _____

_____
_____
_____
_____

What did I savor today? _____

_____
_____
_____
_____

YEAR TWO

BUILDING _the_ BEST YOU THERE IS

What did I do today? _____

_____
_____
_____
_____

What did I feel today? _____

_____
_____
_____
_____

What am I grateful for today? _____

_____
_____
_____
_____

What challenged me today? _____

_____
_____
_____
_____

How can I overcome that challenge? _____

_____
_____
_____
_____

What did I savor today? _____

_____
_____
_____
_____

YEAR ONE

What did I do today? _____

_____
_____
_____
_____

What did I feel today? _____

_____
_____
_____
_____

What am I grateful for today? _____

_____
_____
_____
_____

What challenged me today? _____

_____
_____
_____
_____

How can I overcome that challenge? _____

_____
_____
_____
_____

What did I savor today? _____

_____
_____
_____
_____

YEAR TWO

BUILDING *the* BEST YOU THERE IS

What did I do today? _____

What did I feel today? _____

What am I grateful for today? _____

What challenged me today? _____

How can I overcome that challenge? _____

What did I savor today? _____

What did I do today? _____

What did I feel today? _____

What am I grateful for today? _____

What challenged me today? _____

How can I overcome that challenge? _____

What did I savor today? _____

BUILDING *the* BEST YOU THERE IS

What did I do today? _____

_____

_____

_____

_____

What did I feel today? _____

_____

_____

_____

_____

What am I grateful for today? _____

_____

_____

_____

_____

What challenged me today? _____

_____

_____

_____

_____

How can I overcome that challenge? _____

_____

_____

_____

_____

What did I savor today? _____

_____

_____

_____

_____

What did I do today? _____

_____

_____

_____

_____

What did I feel today? _____

_____

_____

_____

_____

What am I grateful for today? _____

_____

_____

_____

_____

What challenged me today? _____

_____

_____

_____

_____

How can I overcome that challenge? _____

_____

_____

_____

_____

What did I savor today? _____

_____

_____

_____

_____

BUILDING *the* BEST YOU THERE IS

_____ Date

What did I do today? _____

_____

_____

_____

_____

What did I feel today? _____

_____

_____

_____

What am I grateful for today? _____

_____

_____

_____

What challenged me today? _____

_____

_____

_____

How can I overcome that challenge? ____

_____

_____

_____

_____

What did I savor today? _____

_____

_____

_____

YEAR ONE

_____ Date

What did I do today? _____

_____

_____

_____

_____

What did I feel today? _____

_____

_____

_____

What am I grateful for today? _____

_____

_____

_____

What challenged me today? _____

_____

_____

_____

How can I overcome that challenge? ____

_____

_____

_____

_____

What did I savor today? _____

_____

_____

_____

YEAR TWO

BUILDING *the* BEST YOU THERE IS

_____ Date

What did I do today? _____

_____

_____

_____

_____

What did I feel today? _____

_____

_____

_____

_____

What am I grateful for today? _____

_____

_____

_____

What challenged me today? _____

_____

_____

_____

_____

How can I overcome that challenge? _____

_____

_____

_____

_____

What did I savor today? _____

_____

_____

_____

_____

_____ Date

What did I do today? _____

_____

_____

_____

_____

What did I feel today? _____

_____

_____

_____

_____

What am I grateful for today? _____

_____

_____

_____

What challenged me today? _____

_____

_____

_____

_____

How can I overcome that challenge? _____

_____

_____

_____

_____

What did I savor today? _____

_____

_____

_____

_____

BUILDING _the_ BEST YOU THERE IS

_____ Date

What did I do today? _____
_____
_____
_____
_____

What did I feel today? _____
_____
_____
_____

What am I grateful for today? _____
_____
_____
_____

What challenged me today? _____
_____
_____
_____

How can I overcome that challenge? _____
_____
_____
_____

What did I savor today? _____
_____
_____
_____

_____ Date

What did I do today? _____
_____
_____
_____
_____

What did I feel today? _____
_____
_____
_____

What am I grateful for today? _____
_____
_____
_____

What challenged me today? _____
_____
_____
_____

How can I overcome that challenge? _____
_____
_____
_____

What did I savor today? _____
_____
_____
_____

BUILDING the BEST YOU THERE IS

Date

Date

What did I do today? _____	*What did I do today?* _____
_____	_____
_____	_____
_____	_____
What did I feel today? _____	*What did I feel today?* _____
_____	_____
_____	_____
_____	_____
What am I grateful for today? _____	*What am I grateful for today?* _____
_____	_____
_____	_____
_____	_____
What challenged me today? _____	*What challenged me today?* _____
_____	_____
_____	_____
_____	_____
How can I overcome that challenge? ____	*How can I overcome that challenge?* ____
_____	_____
_____	_____
_____	_____
What did I savor today? _____	*What did I savor today?* _____
_____	_____
_____	_____
_____	_____

YEAR ONE

YEAR TWO

BUILDING *the* BEST YOU THERE IS

_____ Date

What did I do today? _____
_____
_____
_____
_____

What did I feel today? _____
_____
_____
_____
_____

What am I grateful for today? _____
_____
_____
_____
_____

What challenged me today? _____
_____
_____
_____
_____

How can I overcome that challenge? _____
_____
_____
_____
_____

What did I savor today? _____
_____
_____
_____
_____

YEAR ONE

_____ Date

What did I do today? _____
_____
_____
_____
_____

What did I feel today? _____
_____
_____
_____
_____

What am I grateful for today? _____
_____
_____
_____
_____

What challenged me today? _____
_____
_____
_____
_____

How can I overcome that challenge? _____
_____
_____
_____
_____

What did I savor today? _____
_____
_____
_____
_____

YEAR TWO

BUILDING *the* BEST YOU THERE IS

What did I do today? _____   *What did I do today?* _____
_____   _____
_____   _____
_____   _____
_____   _____

What did I feel today? _____   *What did I feel today?* _____
_____   _____
_____   _____
_____   _____
_____   _____

What am I grateful for today? _____   *What am I grateful for today?* _____
_____   _____
_____   _____
_____   _____
_____   _____

What challenged me today? _____   *What challenged me today?* _____
_____   _____
_____   _____
_____   _____
_____   _____

How can I overcome that challenge? _____   *How can I overcome that challenge?* _____
_____   _____
_____   _____
_____   _____
_____   _____

What did I savor today? _____   *What did I savor today?* _____
_____   _____
_____   _____
_____   _____
_____   _____

YEAR ONE   YEAR TWO

BUILDING *the* BEST YOU THERE IS

_____ Date   _____ Date

What did I do today? _____   *What did I do today?* _____

_____   _____

_____   _____

_____   _____

_____   _____

What did I feel today? _____   *What did I feel today?* _____

_____   _____

_____   _____

_____   _____

What am I grateful for today? _____   *What am I grateful for today?* _____

_____   _____

_____   _____

_____   _____

What challenged me today? _____   *What challenged me today?* _____

_____   _____

_____   _____

_____   _____

How can I overcome that challenge? _____   *How can I overcome that challenge?* _____

_____   _____

_____   _____

_____   _____

What did I savor today? _____   *What did I savor today?* _____

_____   _____

_____   _____

_____   _____

YEAR ONE   YEAR TWO

BUILDING *the* BEST YOU THERE IS

_____ Date   _____ Date

What did I do today? _____   *What did I do today?* _____

_____   _____

_____   _____

_____   _____

_____   _____

What did I feel today? _____   *What did I feel today?* _____

_____   _____

_____   _____

_____   _____

_____   _____

What am I grateful for today? _____   *What am I grateful for today?* _____

_____   _____

_____   _____

_____   _____

_____   _____

What challenged me today? _____   *What challenged me today?* _____

_____   _____

_____   _____

_____   _____

_____   _____

How can I overcome that challenge? _____   *How can I overcome that challenge?* _____

_____   _____

_____   _____

_____   _____

_____   _____

What did I savor today? _____   *What did I savor today?* _____

_____   _____

_____   _____

_____   _____

_____   _____

YEAR ONE   YEAR TWO

BUILDING *the* BEST YOU THERE IS

_____ Date

What did I do today? _____
_____
_____
_____
_____

What did I feel today? _____
_____
_____
_____

What am I grateful for today? _____
_____
_____
_____

What challenged me today? _____
_____
_____
_____

How can I overcome that challenge? ___
_____
_____
_____

What did I savor today? _____
_____
_____
_____

YEAR ONE

_____ Date

What did I do today? _____
_____
_____
_____
_____

What did I feel today? _____
_____
_____
_____

What am I grateful for today? _____
_____
_____
_____

What challenged me today? _____
_____
_____
_____

How can I overcome that challenge? ___
_____
_____
_____

What did I savor today? _____
_____
_____
_____

YEAR TWO

BUILDING *the* BEST YOU THERE IS

_____ Date

What did I do today? _____

_____
_____
_____
_____

What did I feel today? _____

_____
_____
_____
_____

What am I grateful for today? _____

_____
_____
_____

What challenged me today? _____

_____
_____
_____
_____

How can I overcome that challenge? ____

_____
_____
_____
_____

What did I savor today? _____

_____
_____
_____

YEAR ONE

_____ Date

What did I do today? _____

_____
_____
_____
_____

What did I feel today? _____

_____
_____
_____
_____

What am I grateful for today? _____

_____
_____
_____

What challenged me today? _____

_____
_____
_____
_____

How can I overcome that challenge? ____

_____
_____
_____
_____

What did I savor today? _____

_____
_____
_____

YEAR TWO

BUILDING *the* BEST YOU THERE IS

_____ Date   _____ Date

What did I do today? _____   What did I do today? _____
_____   _____
_____   _____
_____   _____
_____   _____

What did I feel today? _____   What did I feel today? _____
_____   _____
_____   _____
_____   _____

What am I grateful for today? _____   What am I grateful for today? _____
_____   _____
_____   _____
_____   _____

What challenged me today? _____   What challenged me today? _____
_____   _____
_____   _____
_____   _____

How can I overcome that challenge? _____   How can I overcome that challenge? _____
_____   _____
_____   _____
_____   _____

What did I savor today? _____   What did I savor today? _____
_____   _____
_____   _____
_____   _____

BUILDING _the_ BEST YOU THERE IS

What did I do today? _____

What did I do today? _____

_____

_____

_____

_____

_____

_____

_____

_____

What did I feel today? _____

What did I feel today? _____

_____

_____

_____

_____

_____

_____

_____

_____

What am I grateful for today? _____

What am I grateful for today? _____

_____

_____

_____

_____

_____

_____

_____

_____

What challenged me today? _____

What challenged me today? _____

_____

_____

_____

_____

_____

_____

_____

_____

How can I overcome that challenge? _____

How can I overcome that challenge? _____

_____

_____

_____

_____

_____

_____

_____

_____

What did I savor today? _____

What did I savor today? _____

_____

_____

_____

_____

_____

_____

_____

_____

YEAR ONE

YEAR TWO

BUILDING *the* BEST YOU THERE IS

_____ Date

What did I do today? _____
_____
_____
_____

What did I feel today? _____
_____
_____
_____

What am I grateful for today? _____
_____
_____
_____

What challenged me today? _____
_____
_____
_____

How can I overcome that challenge? _____
_____
_____
_____

What did I savor today? _____
_____
_____
_____

YEAR ONE

_____ Date

What did I do today? _____
_____
_____
_____

What did I feel today? _____
_____
_____
_____

What am I grateful for today? _____
_____
_____
_____

What challenged me today? _____
_____
_____
_____

How can I overcome that challenge? _____
_____
_____
_____

What did I savor today? _____
_____
_____
_____

YEAR TWO

BUILDING *the* BEST YOU THERE IS

What did I do today? _____

_____

_____

_____

What did I feel today? _____

_____

_____

_____

What am I grateful for today? _____

_____

_____

_____

What challenged me today? _____

_____

_____

_____

How can I overcome that challenge? _____

_____

_____

_____

What did I savor today? _____

_____

_____

_____

What did I do today? _____

_____

_____

_____

What did I feel today? _____

_____

_____

_____

What am I grateful for today? _____

_____

_____

_____

What challenged me today? _____

_____

_____

_____

How can I overcome that challenge? _____

_____

_____

_____

What did I savor today? _____

_____

_____

_____

YEAR ONE

YEAR TWO

BUILDING *the* BEST YOU THERE IS

What did I do today? _____

_____

_____

_____

_____

What did I feel today? _____

_____

_____

_____

_____

What am I grateful for today? _____

_____

_____

_____

_____

What challenged me today? _____

_____

_____

_____

_____

How can I overcome that challenge? _____

_____

_____

_____

_____

What did I savor today? _____

_____

_____

_____

_____

What did I do today? _____

_____

_____

_____

_____

What did I feel today? _____

_____

_____

_____

_____

What am I grateful for today? _____

_____

_____

_____

_____

What challenged me today? _____

_____

_____

_____

_____

How can I overcome that challenge? _____

_____

_____

_____

_____

What did I savor today? _____

_____

_____

_____

_____

YEAR ONE   YEAR TWO

BUILDING _the_ BEST YOU THERE IS

_____ Date   _____ Date

What did I do today? _____   What did I do today? _____
_____   _____
_____   _____
_____   _____
_____   _____

What did I feel today? _____   What did I feel today? _____
_____   _____
_____   _____
_____   _____
_____   _____

What am I grateful for today? _____ What am I grateful for today? _____
_____   _____
_____   _____
_____   _____
_____   _____

What challenged me today? _____   What challenged me today? _____
_____   _____
_____   _____
_____   _____
_____   _____

How can I overcome that challenge? _____ How can I overcome that challenge? _____
_____   _____
_____   _____
_____   _____
_____   _____

What did I savor today? _____   What did I savor today? _____
_____   _____
_____   _____
_____   _____

YEAR ONE   YEAR TWO

BUILDING *the* BEST YOU THERE IS

_____ Date   _____ Date

What did I do today? _____   *What did I do today?* _____
_____   _____
_____   _____
_____   _____
_____   _____

What did I feel today? _____   *What did I feel today?* _____
_____   _____
_____   _____
_____   _____
_____   _____

What am I grateful for today? _____   *What am I grateful for today?* _____
_____   _____
_____   _____
_____   _____
_____   _____

What challenged me today? _____   *What challenged me today?* _____
_____   _____
_____   _____
_____   _____

How can I overcome that challenge? ____   *How can I overcome that challenge?* ____
_____   _____
_____   _____
_____   _____

What did I savor today? _____   *What did I savor today?* _____
_____   _____
_____   _____
_____   _____

BUILDING *the* BEST YOU THERE IS

What did I do today? _____

_____

_____

_____

_____

What did I feel today? _____

_____

_____

_____

What am I grateful for today? _____

_____

_____

_____

What challenged me today? _____

_____

_____

_____

_____

How can I overcome that challenge? ____

_____

_____

_____

_____

What did I savor today? _____

_____

_____

_____

_____

What did I do today? _____

_____

_____

_____

_____

What did I feel today? _____

_____

_____

_____

What am I grateful for today? _____

_____

_____

_____

What challenged me today? _____

_____

_____

_____

_____

How can I overcome that challenge? ____

_____

_____

_____

_____

What did I savor today? _____

_____

_____

_____

_____

BUILDING *the* BEST YOU THERE IS

_____ Date   _____ Date

What did I do today? _____   *What did I do today?* _____
_____   _____
_____   _____
_____   _____

What did I feel today? _____   *What did I feel today?* _____
_____   _____
_____   _____
_____   _____

What am I grateful for today? _____ *What am I grateful for today?* _____
_____   _____
_____   _____
_____   _____

What challenged me today? _____   *What challenged me today?* _____
_____   _____
_____   _____
_____   _____

How can I overcome that challenge? _____   *How can I overcome that challenge?* _____
_____   _____
_____   _____
_____   _____

What did I savor today? _____   *What did I savor today?* _____
_____   _____
_____   _____
_____   _____

YEAR ONE   YEAR TWO

BUILDING *the* BEST YOU THERE IS

What did I do today? _____

_____

_____

_____

_____

What did I feel today? _____

_____

_____

_____

_____

What am I grateful for today? _____

_____

_____

_____

_____

What challenged me today? _____

_____

_____

_____

_____

How can I overcome that challenge? ____

_____

_____

_____

_____

What did I savor today? _____

_____

_____

_____

_____

What did I do today? _____

_____

_____

_____

_____

What did I feel today? _____

_____

_____

_____

_____

What am I grateful for today? _____

_____

_____

_____

_____

What challenged me today? _____

_____

_____

_____

_____

How can I overcome that challenge? ____

_____

_____

_____

_____

What did I savor today? _____

_____

_____

_____

_____

YEAR ONE   YEAR TWO

BUILDING *the* BEST YOU THERE IS

_____ Date   _____ Date

What did I do today? _____   _What did I do today?_ _____
_____   _____
_____   _____
_____   _____
_____   _____

What did I feel today? _____   _What did I feel today?_ _____
_____   _____
_____   _____
_____   _____
_____   _____

What am I grateful for today? _____   _What am I grateful for today?_ _____
_____   _____
_____   _____
_____   _____
_____   _____

What challenged me today? _____   _What challenged me today?_ _____
_____   _____
_____   _____
_____   _____

How can I overcome that challenge? _____   _How can I overcome that challenge?_ _____
_____   _____
_____   _____
_____   _____

What did I savor today? _____   _What did I savor today?_ _____
_____   _____
_____   _____
_____   _____

YEAR ONE   YEAR TWO

BUILDING _the_ BEST YOU THERE IS

What did I do today? _____

What did I feel today? _____

What am I grateful for today? _____

What challenged me today? _____

How can I overcome that challenge? _____

What did I savor today? _____

What did I do today? _____

What did I feel today? _____

What am I grateful for today? _____

What challenged me today? _____

How can I overcome that challenge? _____

What did I savor today? _____

YEAR ONE

YEAR TWO

BUILDING *the* BEST YOU THERE IS

_____ Date   _____ Date

What did I do today? _____   *What did I do today?* _____
_____   _____
_____   _____
_____   _____

What did I feel today? _____   *What did I feel today?* _____
_____   _____
_____   _____
_____   _____

What am I grateful for today? _____   *What am I grateful for today?* _____
_____   _____
_____   _____
_____   _____

What challenged me today? _____   *What challenged me today?* _____
_____   _____
_____   _____
_____   _____

How can I overcome that challenge? _____   *How can I overcome that challenge?* _____
_____   _____
_____   _____
_____   _____

What did I savor today? _____   *What did I savor today?* _____
_____   _____
_____   _____
_____   _____

YEAR ONE   YEAR TWO

BUILDING *the* BEST YOU THERE IS

_____ Date

What did I do today? _____
_____
_____
_____
_____

What did I feel today? _____
_____
_____
_____
_____

What am I grateful for today? _____
_____
_____
_____

What challenged me today? _____
_____
_____
_____

How can I overcome that challenge? _____
_____
_____
_____

What did I savor today? _____
_____
_____
_____

YEAR ONE

_____ Date

What did I do today? _____
_____
_____
_____
_____

What did I feel today? _____
_____
_____
_____
_____

What am I grateful for today? _____
_____
_____
_____

What challenged me today? _____
_____
_____
_____

How can I overcome that challenge? _____
_____
_____
_____

What did I savor today? _____
_____
_____
_____

YEAR TWO

BUILDING the BEST YOU THERE IS

_____ Date

What did I do today? _____
_____
_____
_____
_____

What did I feel today? _____
_____
_____
_____
_____

What am I grateful for today? _____
_____
_____
_____

What challenged me today? _____
_____
_____
_____
_____

How can I overcome that challenge? _____
_____
_____
_____
_____

What did I savor today? _____
_____
_____
_____
_____

YEAR ONE

_____ Date

What did I do today? _____
_____
_____
_____
_____

What did I feel today? _____
_____
_____
_____
_____

What am I grateful for today? _____
_____
_____
_____

What challenged me today? _____
_____
_____
_____
_____

How can I overcome that challenge? _____
_____
_____
_____
_____

What did I savor today? _____
_____
_____
_____
_____

YEAR TWO

BUILDING _the_ BEST YOU THERE IS

_____ Date

What did I do today? _____

_____
_____
_____
_____

What did I feel today? _____

_____
_____
_____
_____

What am I grateful for today? _____

_____
_____
_____
_____

What challenged me today? _____

_____
_____
_____
_____

How can I overcome that challenge? _____

_____
_____
_____
_____

What did I savor today? _____

_____
_____
_____
_____

Year One

_____ Date

What did I do today? _____

_____
_____
_____
_____

What did I feel today? _____

_____
_____
_____
_____

What am I grateful for today? _____

_____
_____
_____
_____

What challenged me today? _____

_____
_____
_____
_____

How can I overcome that challenge? _____

_____
_____
_____
_____

What did I savor today? _____

_____
_____
_____
_____

Year Two

BUILDING *the* BEST YOU THERE IS

_____ Date   _____ Date

What did I do today? _____   *What did I do today?* _____
_____   _____
_____   _____
_____   _____
_____   _____

What did I feel today? _____   *What did I feel today?* _____
_____   _____
_____   _____
_____   _____
_____   _____

What am I grateful for today? _____   *What am I grateful for today?* _____
_____   _____
_____   _____
_____   _____
_____   _____

What challenged me today? _____   *What challenged me today?* _____
_____   _____
_____   _____
_____   _____
_____   _____

How can I overcome that challenge? _____   *How can I overcome that challenge?* _____
_____   _____
_____   _____
_____   _____
_____   _____

What did I savor today? _____   *What did I savor today?* _____
_____   _____
_____   _____
_____   _____
_____   _____

YEAR ONE   YEAR TWO

BUILDING *the* BEST YOU THERE IS

What did I do today? _____

What did I do today? _____

_____

_____

_____

_____

_____

_____

_____

_____

What did I feel today? _____

What did I feel today? _____

_____

_____

_____

_____

_____

_____

What am I grateful for today? _____

What am I grateful for today? _____

_____

_____

_____

_____

_____

_____

What challenged me today? _____

What challenged me today? _____

_____

_____

_____

_____

_____

_____

How can I overcome that challenge? ____

How can I overcome that challenge? ____

_____

_____

_____

_____

_____

_____

What did I savor today? _____

What did I savor today? _____

_____

_____

_____

_____

_____

_____

BUILDING *the* BEST YOU THERE IS

_____ Date   _____ Date

What did I do today? _____   *What did I do today?* _____
_____   _____
_____   _____
_____   _____
_____   _____

What did I feel today? _____   *What did I feel today?* _____
_____   _____
_____   _____
_____   _____
_____   _____

What am I grateful for today? _____   *What am I grateful for today?* _____
_____   _____
_____   _____
_____   _____
_____   _____

What challenged me today? _____   *What challenged me today?* _____
_____   _____
_____   _____
_____   _____
_____   _____

How can I overcome that challenge? _____ *How can I overcome that challenge?* _____
_____   _____
_____   _____
_____   _____
_____   _____

What did I savor today? _____   *What did I savor today?* _____
_____   _____
_____   _____
_____   _____
_____   _____

YEAR ONE   YEAR TWO

BUILDING *the* BEST YOU THERE IS

_____ Date

What did I do today? _____
_____
_____
_____

What did I feel today? _____
_____
_____
_____

What am I grateful for today? _____
_____
_____
_____

What challenged me today? _____
_____
_____
_____

How can I overcome that challenge? _____
_____
_____
_____

What did I savor today? _____
_____
_____
_____

_____ Date

What did I do today? _____
_____
_____
_____

What did I feel today? _____
_____
_____
_____

What am I grateful for today? _____
_____
_____
_____

What challenged me today? _____
_____
_____
_____

How can I overcome that challenge? _____
_____
_____
_____

What did I savor today? _____
_____
_____
_____

YEAR ONE

YEAR TWO

BUILDING *the* BEST YOU THERE IS

_____ Date

What did I do today? _____
_____
_____
_____

What did I feel today? _____
_____
_____
_____

What am I grateful for today? _____
_____
_____
_____

What challenged me today? _____
_____
_____
_____

How can I overcome that challenge? _____
_____
_____
_____

What did I savor today? _____
_____
_____
_____

_____ Date

What did I do today? _____
_____
_____
_____

What did I feel today? _____
_____
_____
_____

What am I grateful for today? _____
_____
_____
_____

What challenged me today? _____
_____
_____
_____

How can I overcome that challenge? _____
_____
_____
_____

What did I savor today? _____
_____
_____
_____

Do I enjoy spending time with others? _____
_____
_____
_____
_____

Would I like to connect with more people? _____
_____
_____
_____
_____

Do I feel happy when I'm alone? _____
_____
_____
_____
_____

Do I feel safe and secure when I'm by myself? _____
_____
_____
_____
_____

Do I need others to feel whole? _____
_____
_____
_____
_____

Does my life include other people? _____
_____
_____
_____
_____

BUILDING *the* BEST YOU THERE IS

ONE

What was my high point in the preceding weeks? _____

_____

_____

_____

What was the low point? _____

_____

_____

_____

Did the time flow smoothly? _____

_____

_____

_____

Did I create goals? _____

_____

_____

_____

Did I work towards those goals? _____

_____

_____

_____

Did I achieve those goals? _____

_____

_____

_____

_____

Do I enjoy spending time with others? _____

_____

_____

_____

_____

Would I like to connect with more people? _____

_____

_____

_____

_____

Do I feel happy when I'm alone? _____

_____

_____

_____

_____

Do I feel safe and secure when I'm by myself? _____

_____

_____

_____

_____

Do I need others to feel whole? _____

_____

_____

_____

_____

Does my life include other people? _____

_____

_____

_____

_____

What was my high point in the preceding weeks? _____
_____
_____
_____
_____

What was the low point? _____
_____
_____
_____
_____

Did the time flow smoothly? _____
_____
_____
_____
_____

Did I create goals? _____
_____
_____
_____
_____

Did I work towards those goals? _____
_____
_____
_____
_____

Did I achieve those goals? _____
_____
_____
_____
_____

What did I do today? _____

_____

_____

_____

_____

What did I feel today? _____

_____

_____

_____

_____

What am I grateful for today? _____

_____

_____

_____

_____

What challenged me today? _____

_____

_____

_____

_____

How can I overcome that challenge? _____

_____

_____

_____

_____

What did I savor today? _____

_____

_____

_____

_____

What did I do today? _____

_____

_____

_____

_____

What did I feel today? _____

_____

_____

_____

_____

What am I grateful for today? _____

_____

_____

_____

_____

What challenged me today? _____

_____

_____

_____

_____

How can I overcome that challenge? _____

_____

_____

_____

_____

What did I savor today? _____

_____

_____

_____

_____

YEAR ONE

YEAR TWO

BUILDING *the* BEST YOU THERE IS

_____ Date

What did I do today? _____
_____
_____
_____
_____

What did I feel today? _____
_____
_____
_____
_____

What am I grateful for today? _____
_____
_____
_____
_____

What challenged me today? _____
_____
_____
_____
_____

How can I overcome that challenge? _____
_____
_____
_____
_____

What did I savor today? _____
_____
_____
_____
_____

YEAR ONE

_____ Date

What did I do today? _____
_____
_____
_____
_____

What did I feel today? _____
_____
_____
_____
_____

What am I grateful for today? _____
_____
_____
_____
_____

What challenged me today? _____
_____
_____
_____
_____

How can I overcome that challenge? _____
_____
_____
_____
_____

What did I savor today? _____
_____
_____
_____
_____

YEAR TWO

BUILDING _the_ BEST YOU THERE IS

___ Date

What did I do today? _____

_____

_____

_____

_____

What did I feel today? _____

_____

_____

_____

_____

What am I grateful for today? _____

_____

_____

_____

What challenged me today? _____

_____

_____

_____

_____

How can I overcome that challenge? _____

_____

_____

_____

_____

What did I savor today? _____

_____

_____

_____

_____

YEAR ONE

___ Date

What did I do today? _____

_____

_____

_____

_____

What did I feel today? _____

_____

_____

_____

_____

What am I grateful for today? _____

_____

_____

_____

What challenged me today? _____

_____

_____

_____

_____

How can I overcome that challenge? _____

_____

_____

_____

_____

What did I savor today? _____

_____

_____

_____

_____

YEAR TWO

BUILDING *the* BEST YOU THERE IS

_____ Date   _____ Date

What did I do today? _____   What did I do today? _____
_____   _____
_____   _____
_____   _____
_____   _____

What did I feel today? _____   What did I feel today? _____
_____   _____
_____   _____
_____   _____
_____   _____

What am I grateful for today? _____   What am I grateful for today? _____
_____   _____
_____   _____
_____   _____
_____   _____

What challenged me today? _____   What challenged me today? _____
_____   _____
_____   _____
_____   _____
_____   _____

How can I overcome that challenge? ___ How can I overcome that challenge? ___
_____   _____
_____   _____
_____   _____
_____   _____

What did I savor today? _____   What did I savor today? _____
_____   _____
_____   _____
_____   _____

BUILDING *the* BEST YOU THERE IS

_____ Date

What did I do today? _____
_____
_____
_____
_____

What did I feel today? _____
_____
_____
_____
_____

What am I grateful for today? _____
_____
_____
_____
_____

What challenged me today? _____
_____
_____
_____
_____

How can I overcome that challenge? _____
_____
_____
_____
_____

What did I savor today? _____
_____
_____
_____
_____

YEAR ONE

_____ Date

What did I do today? _____
_____
_____
_____
_____

What did I feel today? _____
_____
_____
_____
_____

What am I grateful for today? _____
_____
_____
_____
_____

What challenged me today? _____
_____
_____
_____
_____

How can I overcome that challenge? _____
_____
_____
_____
_____

What did I savor today? _____
_____
_____
_____
_____

YEAR TWO

BUILDING the BEST YOU THERE IS

What did I do today? _____	*What did I do today?* _____
_____	_____
_____	_____
_____	_____
_____	_____
What did I feel today? _____	*What did I feel today?* _____
_____	_____
_____	_____
_____	_____
_____	_____
What am I grateful for today? _____	*What am I grateful for today?* _____
_____	_____
_____	_____
_____	_____
_____	_____
What challenged me today? _____	*What challenged me today?* _____
_____	_____
_____	_____
_____	_____
_____	_____
How can I overcome that challenge? ___	*How can I overcome that challenge?* ___
_____	_____
_____	_____
_____	_____
_____	_____
What did I savor today? _____	*What did I savor today?* _____
_____	_____
_____	_____
_____	_____

What did I do today? _____

_____

_____

_____

_____

What did I feel today? _____

_____

_____

_____

_____

What am I grateful for today? _____

_____

_____

_____

What challenged me today? _____

_____

_____

_____

_____

How can I overcome that challenge? _____

_____

_____

_____

_____

What did I savor today? _____

_____

_____

_____

_____

What did I do today? _____

_____

_____

_____

_____

What did I feel today? _____

_____

_____

_____

_____

What am I grateful for today? _____

_____

_____

_____

What challenged me today? _____

_____

_____

_____

_____

How can I overcome that challenge? _____

_____

_____

_____

_____

What did I savor today? _____

_____

_____

_____

_____

YEAR ONE

YEAR TWO

BUILDING *the* BEST YOU THERE IS

_____ Date

What did I do today? _____

_____

_____

_____

_____

What did I feel today? _____

_____

_____

_____

_____

What am I grateful for today? _____

_____

_____

_____

_____

What challenged me today? _____

_____

_____

_____

_____

How can I overcome that challenge? _____

_____

_____

_____

_____

What did I savor today? _____

_____

_____

_____

_____

YEAR ONE

_____ Date

What did I do today? _____

_____

_____

_____

_____

What did I feel today? _____

_____

_____

_____

_____

What am I grateful for today? _____

_____

_____

_____

_____

What challenged me today? _____

_____

_____

_____

_____

How can I overcome that challenge? _____

_____

_____

_____

_____

What did I savor today? _____

_____

_____

_____

_____

YEAR TWO

BUILDING _the_ BEST YOU THERE IS

What did I do today? _____

What did I do today? _____

What did I feel today? _____

What did I feel today? _____

What am I grateful for today? _____

What am I grateful for today? _____

What challenged me today? _____

What challenged me today? _____

How can I overcome that challenge? _____

How can I overcome that challenge? _____

What did I savor today? _____

What did I savor today? _____

_____ Date

What did I do today? _____

_____

_____

_____

_____

What did I feel today? _____

_____

_____

_____

_____

What am I grateful for today? _____

_____

_____

_____

_____

What challenged me today? _____

_____

_____

_____

_____

How can I overcome that challenge? _____

_____

_____

_____

_____

What did I savor today? _____

_____

_____

_____

_____ Date

What did I do today? _____

_____

_____

_____

_____

What did I feel today? _____

_____

_____

_____

_____

What am I grateful for today? _____

_____

_____

_____

_____

What challenged me today? _____

_____

_____

_____

_____

How can I overcome that challenge? _____

_____

_____

_____

_____

What did I savor today? _____

_____

_____

_____

YEAR ONE   YEAR TWO

BUILDING _the_ BEST YOU THERE IS

_____ Date

What did I do today? _____

_____
_____
_____

What did I feel today? _____

_____
_____
_____

What am I grateful for today? _____

_____
_____
_____

What challenged me today? _____

_____
_____
_____

How can I overcome that challenge? _____

_____
_____
_____

What did I savor today? _____

_____
_____
_____

YEAR ONE

_____ Date

What did I do today? _____

_____
_____
_____

What did I feel today? _____

_____
_____
_____

What am I grateful for today? _____

_____
_____
_____

What challenged me today? _____

_____
_____
_____

How can I overcome that challenge? _____

_____
_____
_____

What did I savor today? _____

_____
_____
_____

YEAR TWO

BUILDING _the_ BEST YOU THERE IS

_____ Date

_____ Date

What did I do today? _____

_____
_____
_____
_____

What did I feel today? _____

_____
_____
_____
_____

What am I grateful for today? _____

_____
_____
_____
_____

What challenged me today? _____

_____
_____
_____
_____

How can I overcome that challenge? _____

_____
_____
_____
_____

What did I savor today? _____

_____
_____
_____
_____

What did I do today? _____

_____
_____
_____
_____

What did I feel today? _____

_____
_____
_____
_____

What am I grateful for today? _____

_____
_____
_____
_____

What challenged me today? _____

_____
_____
_____
_____

How can I overcome that challenge? _____

_____
_____
_____
_____

What did I savor today? _____

_____
_____
_____
_____

YEAR ONE

YEAR TWO

BUILDING *the* BEST YOU THERE IS

What did I do today? _____   What did I do today? _____
_____   _____
_____   _____
_____   _____

What did I feel today? _____   What did I feel today? _____
_____   _____
_____   _____
_____   _____

What am I grateful for today? _____   What am I grateful for today? _____
_____   _____
_____   _____
_____   _____

What challenged me today? _____   What challenged me today? _____
_____   _____
_____   _____
_____   _____

How can I overcome that challenge? _____   How can I overcome that challenge? _____
_____   _____
_____   _____
_____   _____

What did I savor today? _____   What did I savor today? _____
_____   _____
_____   _____
_____   _____

_____ Date

What did I do today? _____

_____

_____

_____

_____

What did I feel today? _____

_____

_____

_____

_____

What am I grateful for today? _____

_____

_____

_____

_____

What challenged me today? _____

_____

_____

_____

_____

How can I overcome that challenge? _____

_____

_____

_____

_____

What did I savor today? _____

_____

_____

_____

_____

YEAR ONE

_____ Date

What did I do today? _____

_____

_____

_____

_____

What did I feel today? _____

_____

_____

_____

_____

What am I grateful for today? _____

_____

_____

_____

_____

What challenged me today? _____

_____

_____

_____

_____

How can I overcome that challenge? _____

_____

_____

_____

_____

What did I savor today? _____

_____

_____

_____

_____

YEAR TWO

BUILDING _the_ BEST YOU THERE IS

_____ Date   _____ Date

What did I do today? _____   What did I do today? _____
_____   _____
_____   _____
_____   _____

What did I feel today? _____   What did I feel today? _____
_____   _____
_____   _____
_____   _____

What am I grateful for today? _____   What am I grateful for today? _____
_____   _____
_____   _____
_____   _____

What challenged me today? _____   What challenged me today? _____
_____   _____
_____   _____
_____   _____

How can I overcome that challenge? _____   How can I overcome that challenge? _____
_____   _____
_____   _____
_____   _____

What did I savor today? _____   What did I savor today? _____
_____   _____
_____   _____
_____   _____

YEAR ONE   YEAR TWO

BUILDING _the_ BEST YOU THERE IS

What did I do today? _____

What did I do today? _____

_____

_____

_____

_____

_____

_____

_____

_____

What did I feel today? _____

What did I feel today? _____

_____

_____

_____

_____

_____

_____

What am I grateful for today? _____

What am I grateful for today? _____

_____

_____

_____

_____

_____

_____

What challenged me today? _____

What challenged me today? _____

_____

_____

_____

_____

_____

_____

How can I overcome that challenge? _____

How can I overcome that challenge? _____

_____

_____

_____

_____

_____

_____

What did I savor today? _____

What did I savor today? _____

_____

_____

_____

_____

_____

_____

YEAR ONE

YEAR TWO

BUILDING *the* BEST YOU THERE IS

_____ Date   _____ Date

What did I do today? _____   *What did I do today?* _____
_____   _____
_____   _____
_____   _____
_____   _____

What did I feel today? _____   *What did I feel today?* _____
_____   _____
_____   _____
_____   _____
_____   _____

What am I grateful for today? _____   *What am I grateful for today?* _____
_____   _____
_____   _____
_____   _____
_____   _____

What challenged me today? _____   *What challenged me today?* _____
_____   _____
_____   _____
_____   _____
_____   _____

How can I overcome that challenge? _____ *How can I overcome that challenge?* _____
_____   _____
_____   _____
_____   _____
_____   _____

What did I savor today? _____   *What did I savor today?* _____
_____   _____
_____   _____
_____   _____
_____   _____

YEAR ONE   YEAR TWO

_____ Date   _____ Date

What did I do today? _____   What did I do today? _____

_____   _____

_____   _____

_____   _____

What did I feel today? _____   What did I feel today? _____

_____   _____

_____   _____

_____   _____

What am I grateful for today? _____   What am I grateful for today? _____

_____   _____

_____   _____

_____   _____

What challenged me today? _____   What challenged me today? _____

_____   _____

_____   _____

_____   _____

How can I overcome that challenge? _____   How can I overcome that challenge? _____

_____   _____

_____   _____

_____   _____

What did I savor today? _____   What did I savor today? _____

_____   _____

_____   _____

_____   _____

YEAR ONE   YEAR TWO

BUILDING _the_ BEST YOU THERE IS

_____ Date

What did I do today? _____
_____
_____
_____
_____

What did I feel today? _____
_____
_____
_____
_____

What am I grateful for today? _____
_____
_____
_____
_____

What challenged me today? _____
_____
_____
_____
_____

How can I overcome that challenge? _____
_____
_____
_____
_____

What did I savor today? _____
_____
_____
_____
_____

YEAR ONE

_____ Date

What did I do today? _____
_____
_____
_____
_____

What did I feel today? _____
_____
_____
_____
_____

What am I grateful for today? _____
_____
_____
_____
_____

What challenged me today? _____
_____
_____
_____
_____

How can I overcome that challenge? _____
_____
_____
_____
_____

What did I savor today? _____
_____
_____
_____
_____

YEAR TWO

BUILDING *the* BEST YOU THERE IS

_____ Date

What did I do today? _____
_____
_____
_____
_____

What did I feel today? _____
_____
_____
_____
_____

What am I grateful for today? _____
_____
_____
_____
_____

What challenged me today? _____
_____
_____
_____
_____

How can I overcome that challenge? _____
_____
_____
_____
_____

What did I savor today? _____
_____
_____
_____
_____

YEAR ONE

_____ Date

What did I do today? _____
_____
_____
_____
_____

What did I feel today? _____
_____
_____
_____
_____

What am I grateful for today? _____
_____
_____
_____
_____

What challenged me today? _____
_____
_____
_____
_____

How can I overcome that challenge? _____
_____
_____
_____
_____

What did I savor today? _____
_____
_____
_____
_____

YEAR TWO

BUILDING _the_ BEST YOU THERE IS

What did I do today? _____

_____

_____

_____

_____

What did I feel today? _____

_____

_____

_____

What am I grateful for today? _____

_____

_____

_____

What challenged me today? _____

_____

_____

_____

_____

How can I overcome that challenge? _____

_____

_____

_____

What did I savor today? _____

_____

_____

_____

YEAR ONE

_____ Date

What did I do today? _____

_____

_____

_____

_____

What did I feel today? _____

_____

_____

_____

What am I grateful for today? _____

_____

_____

_____

What challenged me today? _____

_____

_____

_____

_____

How can I overcome that challenge? _____

_____

_____

_____

What did I savor today? _____

_____

_____

_____

YEAR TWO

What did I do today? _____   What did I do today? _____
_____   _____
_____   _____
_____   _____

What did I feel today? _____   What did I feel today? _____
_____   _____
_____   _____
_____   _____

What am I grateful for today? _____   What am I grateful for today? _____
_____   _____
_____   _____
_____   _____

What challenged me today? _____   What challenged me today? _____
_____   _____
_____   _____
_____   _____

How can I overcome that challenge? _____   How can I overcome that challenge? _____
_____   _____
_____   _____
_____   _____

What did I savor today? _____   What did I savor today? _____
_____   _____
_____   _____
_____   _____

YEAR ONE   YEAR TWO

BUILDING *the* BEST YOU THERE IS

_____ Date

What did I do today? _____

_____

_____

_____

What did I feel today? _____

_____

_____

_____

What am I grateful for today? _____

_____

_____

_____

What challenged me today? _____

_____

_____

_____

How can I overcome that challenge? _____

_____

_____

_____

What did I savor today? _____

_____

_____

_____

YEAR ONE

_____ Date

What did I do today? _____

_____

_____

_____

What did I feel today? _____

_____

_____

_____

What am I grateful for today? _____

_____

_____

_____

What challenged me today? _____

_____

_____

_____

How can I overcome that challenge? _____

_____

_____

_____

What did I savor today? _____

_____

_____

_____

YEAR TWO

BUILDING *the* BEST YOU THERE IS

What did I do today? _____   What did I do today? _____
_____   _____
_____   _____
_____   _____

What did I feel today? _____   What did I feel today? _____
_____   _____
_____   _____
_____   _____

What am I grateful for today? _____   What am I grateful for today? _____
_____   _____
_____   _____
_____   _____

What challenged me today? _____   What challenged me today? _____
_____   _____
_____   _____
_____   _____

How can I overcome that challenge? _____   How can I overcome that challenge? _____
_____   _____
_____   _____
_____   _____

What did I savor today? _____   What did I savor today? _____
_____   _____
_____   _____
_____   _____

Date _____

What did I do today? _____
_____
_____
_____
_____

What did I feel today? _____
_____
_____
_____

What am I grateful for today? _____
_____
_____
_____

What challenged me today? _____
_____
_____
_____
_____

How can I overcome that challenge? _____
_____
_____
_____
_____

What did I savor today? _____
_____
_____
_____
_____

Date _____

What did I do today? _____
_____
_____
_____
_____

What did I feel today? _____
_____
_____
_____

What am I grateful for today? _____
_____
_____
_____

What challenged me today? _____
_____
_____
_____
_____

How can I overcome that challenge? _____
_____
_____
_____
_____

What did I savor today? _____
_____
_____
_____
_____

BUILDING *the* BEST YOU THERE IS

_____ Date

What did I do today? _____
_____
_____
_____
_____

What did I feel today? _____
_____
_____
_____

What am I grateful for today? _____
_____
_____
_____

What challenged me today? _____
_____
_____
_____

How can I overcome that challenge? _____
_____
_____
_____

What did I savor today? _____
_____
_____
_____

YEAR ONE

_____ Date

What did I do today? _____
_____
_____
_____
_____

What did I feel today? _____
_____
_____
_____

What am I grateful for today? _____
_____
_____
_____

What challenged me today? _____
_____
_____
_____

How can I overcome that challenge? _____
_____
_____
_____

What did I savor today? _____
_____
_____
_____

YEAR TWO

BUILDING _the_ BEST YOU THERE IS

_____ Date

What did I do today? _____
_____
_____
_____

What did I feel today? _____
_____
_____
_____

What am I grateful for today? _____
_____
_____
_____

What challenged me today? _____
_____
_____
_____

How can I overcome that challenge? _____
_____
_____
_____

What did I savor today? _____
_____
_____
_____

YEAR ONE

_____ Date

What did I do today? _____
_____
_____
_____

What did I feel today? _____
_____
_____
_____

What am I grateful for today? _____
_____
_____
_____

What challenged me today? _____
_____
_____
_____

How can I overcome that challenge? _____
_____
_____
_____

What did I savor today? _____
_____
_____
_____

YEAR TWO

BUILDING *the* BEST YOU THERE IS

_____ Date

What did I do today? _____
_____
_____
_____

What did I feel today? _____
_____
_____
_____

What am I grateful for today? _____
_____
_____
_____

What challenged me today? _____
_____
_____
_____

How can I overcome that challenge? _____
_____
_____
_____

What did I savor today? _____
_____
_____
_____

YEAR ONE

_____ Date

What did I do today? _____
_____
_____
_____

What did I feel today? _____
_____
_____
_____

What am I grateful for today? _____
_____
_____
_____

What challenged me today? _____
_____
_____
_____

How can I overcome that challenge? _____
_____
_____
_____

What did I savor today? _____
_____
_____
_____

YEAR TWO

BUILDING _the_ BEST YOU THERE IS

_____ Date

What did I do today? _____
_____
_____
_____
_____

What did I feel today? _____
_____
_____
_____
_____

What am I grateful for today? _____
_____
_____
_____
_____

What challenged me today? _____
_____
_____
_____
_____

How can I overcome that challenge? _____
_____
_____
_____
_____

What did I savor today? _____
_____
_____
_____
_____

YEAR ONE

_____ Date

What did I do today? _____
_____
_____
_____
_____

What did I feel today? _____
_____
_____
_____
_____

What am I grateful for today? _____
_____
_____
_____
_____

What challenged me today? _____
_____
_____
_____
_____

How can I overcome that challenge? _____
_____
_____
_____
_____

What did I savor today? _____
_____
_____
_____
_____

YEAR TWO

BUILDING _the_ BEST YOU THERE IS

_____ Date	_____ Date

What did I do today? _____

_____

_____

_____

_____

What did I feel today? _____

_____

_____

_____

What am I grateful for today? _____

_____

_____

_____

What challenged me today? _____

_____

_____

_____

How can I overcome that challenge? _____

_____

_____

_____

What did I savor today? _____

_____

_____

_____

What did I do today? _____

_____

_____

_____

_____

What did I feel today? _____

_____

_____

_____

What am I grateful for today? _____

_____

_____

_____

What challenged me today? _____

_____

_____

_____

How can I overcome that challenge? _____

_____

_____

_____

What did I savor today? _____

_____

_____

_____

What did I do today? _____   What did I do today? _____
_____   _____
_____   _____
_____   _____

What did I feel today? _____   What did I feel today? _____
_____   _____
_____   _____
_____   _____

What am I grateful for today? _____   What am I grateful for today? _____
_____   _____
_____   _____
_____   _____

What challenged me today? _____   What challenged me today? _____
_____   _____
_____   _____
_____   _____

How can I overcome that challenge? ___   How can I overcome that challenge? ___
_____   _____
_____   _____
_____   _____

What did I savor today? _____   What did I savor today? _____
_____   _____
_____   _____
_____   _____

BUILDING *the* BEST YOU THERE IS

What did I do today? _____
_____
_____
_____
_____

What did I feel today? _____
_____
_____
_____
_____

What am I grateful for today? _____
_____
_____
_____
_____

What challenged me today? _____
_____
_____
_____
_____

How can I overcome that challenge? _____
_____
_____
_____
_____

What did I savor today? _____
_____
_____
_____
_____

YEAR ONE

What did I do today? _____
_____
_____
_____
_____

What did I feel today? _____
_____
_____
_____
_____

What am I grateful for today? _____
_____
_____
_____
_____

What challenged me today? _____
_____
_____
_____
_____

How can I overcome that challenge? _____
_____
_____
_____
_____

What did I savor today? _____
_____
_____
_____
_____

YEAR TWO

BUILDING *the* BEST YOU THERE IS

What did I do today? _____   What did I do today? _____
_____   _____
_____   _____
_____   _____
_____   _____

What did I feel today? _____   What did I feel today? _____
_____   _____
_____   _____
_____   _____

What am I grateful for today? _____   What am I grateful for today? _____
_____   _____
_____   _____
_____   _____

What challenged me today? _____   What challenged me today? _____
_____   _____
_____   _____
_____   _____

How can I overcome that challenge? _____   How can I overcome that challenge? _____
_____   _____
_____   _____
_____   _____

What did I savor today? _____   What did I savor today? _____
_____   _____
_____   _____
_____   _____

YEAR ONE   YEAR TWO

BUILDING *the* BEST YOU THERE IS

_____ Date

What did I do today? _____

_____
_____
_____

What did I feel today? _____

_____
_____
_____

What am I grateful for today? _____

_____
_____
_____

What challenged me today? _____

_____
_____
_____

How can I overcome that challenge? _____

_____
_____
_____

What did I savor today? _____

_____
_____
_____

YEAR ONE

_____ Date

What did I do today? _____

_____
_____
_____

What did I feel today? _____

_____
_____
_____

What am I grateful for today? _____

_____
_____
_____

What challenged me today? _____

_____
_____
_____

How can I overcome that challenge? _____

_____
_____
_____

What did I savor today? _____

_____
_____
_____

YEAR TWO

BUILDING *the* BEST YOU THERE IS

Date

What did I do today? _____
_____
_____
_____
_____

What did I feel today? _____
_____
_____
_____
_____

What am I grateful for today? _____
_____
_____
_____
_____

What challenged me today? _____
_____
_____
_____
_____

How can I overcome that challenge? ____
_____
_____
_____
_____

What did I savor today? _____
_____
_____
_____
_____

Date

What did I do today? _____
_____
_____
_____
_____

What did I feel today? _____
_____
_____
_____
_____

What am I grateful for today? _____
_____
_____
_____
_____

What challenged me today? _____
_____
_____
_____
_____

How can I overcome that challenge? ____
_____
_____
_____
_____

What did I savor today? _____
_____
_____
_____
_____

_____ Date   _____ Date

What did I do today? _____   What did I do today? _____

_____   _____

_____   _____

_____   _____

What did I feel today? _____   What did I feel today? _____

_____   _____

_____   _____

_____   _____

What am I grateful for today? _____   What am I grateful for today? _____

_____   _____

_____   _____

_____   _____

What challenged me today? _____   What challenged me today? _____

_____   _____

_____   _____

_____   _____

How can I overcome that challenge? _____   How can I overcome that challenge? _____

_____   _____

_____   _____

_____   _____

What did I savor today? _____   What did I savor today? _____

_____   _____

_____   _____

_____   _____

YEAR ONE   YEAR TWO

BUILDING _the_ BEST YOU THERE IS

                                              Date   Date

What did I do today? _____   What did I do today? _____
_____   _____
_____   _____
_____   _____
_____   _____

What did I feel today? _____   What did I feel today? _____
_____   _____
_____   _____
_____   _____
_____   _____

What am I grateful for today? _____   What am I grateful for today? _____
_____   _____
_____   _____
_____   _____
_____   _____

What challenged me today? _____   What challenged me today? _____
_____   _____
_____   _____
_____   _____
_____   _____

How can I overcome that challenge? _____   How can I overcome that challenge? _____
_____   _____
_____   _____
_____   _____
_____   _____

What did I savor today? _____   What did I savor today? _____
_____   _____
_____   _____
_____   _____

                                  YEAR ONE   YEAR TWO
                        BUILDING *the* BEST YOU THERE IS

_____ Date

What did I do today? _____
_____
_____
_____
_____

What did I feel today? _____
_____
_____
_____
_____

What am I grateful for today? _____
_____
_____
_____
_____

What challenged me today? _____
_____
_____
_____
_____

How can I overcome that challenge? _____
_____
_____
_____
_____

What did I savor today? _____
_____
_____
_____
_____

YEAR ONE

_____ Date

What did I do today? _____
_____
_____
_____
_____

What did I feel today? _____
_____
_____
_____
_____

What am I grateful for today? _____
_____
_____
_____
_____

What challenged me today? _____
_____
_____
_____
_____

How can I overcome that challenge? _____
_____
_____
_____
_____

What did I savor today? _____
_____
_____
_____
_____

YEAR TWO

BUILDING _the_ BEST YOU THERE IS

_____ Date   _____ Date

What did I do today? _____   *What did I do today?* _____
_____   _____
_____   _____
_____   _____

What did I feel today? _____   *What did I feel today?* _____
_____   _____
_____   _____
_____   _____

What am I grateful for today? _____ *What am I grateful for today?* _____
_____   _____
_____   _____
_____   _____

What challenged me today? _____   *What challenged me today?* _____
_____   _____
_____   _____
_____   _____

How can I overcome that challenge? _____   *How can I overcome that challenge?* _____
_____   _____
_____   _____
_____   _____

What did I savor today? _____   *What did I savor today?* _____
_____   _____
_____   _____
_____   _____

YEAR ONE   YEAR TWO

BUILDING *the* BEST YOU THERE IS

_____ Date

What did I do today? _____
_____
_____
_____
_____

What did I feel today? _____
_____
_____
_____
_____

What am I grateful for today? _____
_____
_____
_____
_____

What challenged me today? _____
_____
_____
_____
_____

How can I overcome that challenge? ___
_____
_____
_____
_____

What did I savor today? _____
_____
_____
_____
_____

YEAR ONE

_____ Date

What did I do today? _____
_____
_____
_____
_____

What did I feel today? _____
_____
_____
_____
_____

What am I grateful for today? _____
_____
_____
_____
_____

What challenged me today? _____
_____
_____
_____
_____

How can I overcome that challenge? ___
_____
_____
_____
_____

What did I savor today? _____
_____
_____
_____
_____

YEAR TWO

BUILDING _the_ BEST YOU THERE IS

_____ Date

What did I do today? _____

_____

_____

_____

What did I feel today? _____

_____

_____

_____

What am I grateful for today? _____

_____

_____

_____

What challenged me today? _____

_____

_____

_____

How can I overcome that challenge? ____

_____

_____

_____

What did I savor today? _____

_____

_____

_____

YEAR ONE

_____ Date

What did I do today? _____

_____

_____

_____

What did I feel today? _____

_____

_____

_____

What am I grateful for today? _____

_____

_____

_____

What challenged me today? _____

_____

_____

_____

How can I overcome that challenge? ____

_____

_____

_____

What did I savor today? _____

_____

_____

_____

YEAR TWO

BUILDING the BEST YOU THERE IS

_____ Date

What did I do today? _____
_____
_____
_____
_____

What did I feel today? _____
_____
_____
_____
_____

What am I grateful for today? _____
_____
_____
_____
_____

What challenged me today? _____
_____
_____
_____
_____

How can I overcome that challenge? _____
_____
_____
_____
_____

What did I savor today? _____
_____
_____
_____
_____

YEAR ONE

_____ Date

What did I do today? _____
_____
_____
_____
_____

What did I feel today? _____
_____
_____
_____
_____

What am I grateful for today? _____
_____
_____
_____
_____

What challenged me today? _____
_____
_____
_____
_____

How can I overcome that challenge? _____
_____
_____
_____
_____

What did I savor today? _____
_____
_____
_____
_____

YEAR TWO

BUILDING the BEST YOU THERE IS

_____ Date   _____ Date

What did I do today? _____ *What did I do today?* _____
_____ _____
_____ _____
_____ _____

What did I feel today? _____ *What did I feel today?* _____
_____ _____
_____ _____
_____ _____

What am I grateful for today? _____ *What am I grateful for today?* _____
_____ _____
_____ _____
_____ _____

What challenged me today? _____ *What challenged me today?* _____
_____ _____
_____ _____
_____ _____

How can I overcome that challenge? _____ *How can I overcome that challenge?* _____
_____ _____
_____ _____
_____ _____

What did I savor today? _____ *What did I savor today?* _____
_____ _____
_____ _____
_____ _____

YEAR ONE   YEAR TWO

BUILDING *the* BEST YOU THERE IS

_____ Date   _____ Date

What did I do today? _____   *What did I do today?* _____
_____   _____
_____   _____
_____   _____
_____   _____

What did I feel today? _____   *What did I feel today?* _____
_____   _____
_____   _____
_____   _____

What am I grateful for today? _____   *What am I grateful for today?* _____
_____   _____
_____   _____
_____   _____

What challenged me today? _____   *What challenged me today?* _____
_____   _____
_____   _____
_____   _____

How can I overcome that challenge? ___   *How can I overcome that challenge?* ___
_____   _____
_____   _____
_____   _____
_____   _____

What did I savor today? _____   *What did I savor today?* _____
_____   _____
_____   _____
_____   _____

YEAR ONE   YEAR TWO

BUILDING *the* BEST YOU THERE IS

Do I feel loved? _____

_____

_____

_____

_____

Do I rely on others for love? _____

_____

_____

_____

_____

Am I in search of deeper love? _____

_____

_____

_____

_____

Do I know how to achieve deep love? _____

_____

_____

_____

_____

Am I in touch with my feelings? _____

_____

_____

_____

_____

What would bring me more love? _____

_____

_____

_____

_____

Do I believe in havingness? _____

_____

_____

_____

_____

Am I creating prosperity? _____

_____

_____

_____

Could my life be easier? _____

_____

_____

_____

What can I do to make it easier? _____

_____

_____

_____

Do I have everything I need? _____

_____

_____

_____

Do I have everything I want? _____

_____

_____

_____

BUILDING *the* BEST YOU THERE IS

Do I feel loved? _____

_____

_____

_____

_____

Do I rely on others for love? _____

_____

_____

_____

_____

Am I in search of deeper love? _____

_____

_____

_____

_____

Do I know how to achieve deep love? _____

_____

_____

_____

_____

Am I in touch with my feelings? _____

_____

_____

_____

_____

What would bring me more love? _____

_____

_____

_____

_____

BUILDING *the* BEST YOU THERE IS

TWO

Do I believe in havingness? _____

Am I creating prosperity? _____

Could my life be easier? _____

What can I do to make it easier? _____

Do I have everything I need? _____

Do I have everything I want? _____

_____ Date   _____ Date

What did I do today? _____   *What did I do today?* _____
_____   _____
_____   _____
_____   _____
_____   _____

What did I feel today? _____   *What did I feel today?* _____
_____   _____
_____   _____
_____   _____
_____   _____

What am I grateful for today? _____   *What am I grateful for today?* _____
_____   _____
_____   _____
_____   _____
_____   _____

What challenged me today? _____   *What challenged me today?* _____
_____   _____
_____   _____
_____   _____
_____   _____

How can I overcome that challenge? _____ *How can I overcome that challenge?* _____
_____   _____
_____   _____
_____   _____
_____   _____

What did I savor today? _____   *What did I savor today?* _____
_____   _____
_____   _____
_____   _____

YEAR ONE   YEAR TWO

BUILDING *the* BEST YOU THERE IS

What did I do today? _____   *What did I do today?* _____

_____   _____

_____   _____

_____   _____

What did I feel today? _____   *What did I feel today?* _____

_____   _____

_____   _____

_____   _____

What am I grateful for today? _____   *What am I grateful for today?* _____

_____   _____

_____   _____

_____   _____

What challenged me today? _____   *What challenged me today?* _____

_____   _____

_____   _____

_____   _____

How can I overcome that challenge? _____   *How can I overcome that challenge?* _____

_____   _____

_____   _____

_____   _____

What did I savor today? _____   *What did I savor today?* _____

_____   _____

_____   _____

_____   _____

BUILDING *the* BEST YOU THERE IS

_____ Date

_____ Date

What did I do today? _____

What did I do today? _____

_____

_____

_____

_____

_____

_____

What did I feel today? _____

What did I feel today? _____

_____

_____

_____

_____

_____

_____

What am I grateful for today? _____

What am I grateful for today? _____

_____

_____

_____

_____

_____

_____

What challenged me today? _____

What challenged me today? _____

_____

_____

_____

_____

_____

_____

How can I overcome that challenge? _____

How can I overcome that challenge? _____

_____

_____

_____

_____

_____

_____

What did I savor today? _____

What did I savor today? _____

_____

_____

_____

_____

_____

_____

YEAR ONE

YEAR TWO

BUILDING *the* BEST YOU THERE IS

_____ Date

What did I do today? _____
_____
_____
_____

What did I feel today? _____
_____
_____
_____

What am I grateful for today? _____
_____
_____
_____

What challenged me today? _____
_____
_____
_____

How can I overcome that challenge? _____
_____
_____
_____

What did I savor today? _____
_____
_____
_____

YEAR ONE

_____ Date

What did I do today? _____
_____
_____
_____

What did I feel today? _____
_____
_____
_____

What am I grateful for today? _____
_____
_____
_____

What challenged me today? _____
_____
_____
_____

How can I overcome that challenge? _____
_____
_____
_____

What did I savor today? _____
_____
_____
_____

YEAR TWO

BUILDING _the_ BEST YOU THERE IS

_____ Date

What did I do today? _____

_____

_____

_____

_____

What did I feel today? _____

_____

_____

_____

_____

What am I grateful for today? _____

_____

_____

_____

_____

What challenged me today? _____

_____

_____

_____

_____

How can I overcome that challenge? _____

_____

_____

_____

_____

What did I savor today? _____

_____

_____

_____

_____

YEAR ONE

_____ Date

What did I do today? _____

_____

_____

_____

_____

What did I feel today? _____

_____

_____

_____

_____

What am I grateful for today? _____

_____

_____

_____

_____

What challenged me today? _____

_____

_____

_____

_____

How can I overcome that challenge? _____

_____

_____

_____

_____

What did I savor today? _____

_____

_____

_____

_____

YEAR TWO

BUILDING _the_ BEST YOU THERE IS

_____ Date

What did I do today? _____
_____
_____
_____

What did I feel today? _____
_____
_____
_____

What am I grateful for today? _____
_____
_____
_____

What challenged me today? _____
_____
_____
_____

How can I overcome that challenge? _____
_____
_____
_____

What did I savor today? _____
_____
_____
_____

YEAR ONE

_____ Date

What did I do today? _____
_____
_____
_____

What did I feel today? _____
_____
_____
_____

What am I grateful for today? _____
_____
_____
_____

What challenged me today? _____
_____
_____
_____

How can I overcome that challenge? _____
_____
_____
_____

What did I savor today? _____
_____
_____
_____

YEAR TWO

BUILDING _the_ BEST YOU THERE IS

_____ Date   _____ Date

What did I do today? _____   *What did I do today?* _____
_____   _____
_____   _____
_____   _____
_____   _____

What did I feel today? _____   *What did I feel today?* _____
_____   _____
_____   _____
_____   _____
_____   _____

What am I grateful for today? _____ *What am I grateful for today?* _____
_____   _____
_____   _____
_____   _____
_____   _____

What challenged me today? _____   *What challenged me today?* _____
_____   _____
_____   _____
_____   _____
_____   _____

How can I overcome that challenge? _____   *How can I overcome that challenge?* _____
_____   _____
_____   _____
_____   _____
_____   _____

What did I savor today? _____   *What did I savor today?* _____
_____   _____
_____   _____
_____   _____
_____   _____

YEAR ONE   YEAR TWO

BUILDING *the* BEST YOU THERE IS

Date

Date

What did I do today? _____   What did I do today? _____

_____   _____
_____   _____
_____   _____

What did I feel today? _____   What did I feel today? _____

_____   _____
_____   _____
_____   _____

What am I grateful for today? _____   What am I grateful for today? _____

_____   _____
_____   _____
_____   _____

What challenged me today? _____   What challenged me today? _____

_____   _____
_____   _____
_____   _____

How can I overcome that challenge? __   How can I overcome that challenge? __

_____   _____
_____   _____
_____   _____

What did I savor today? _____   What did I savor today? _____

_____   _____
_____   _____
_____   _____

_____ Date

What did I do today? _____
_____
_____
_____

What did I feel today? _____
_____
_____
_____

What am I grateful for today? _____
_____
_____
_____

What challenged me today? _____
_____
_____
_____

How can I overcome that challenge? _____
_____
_____
_____

What did I savor today? _____
_____
_____
_____

_____ Date

What did I do today? _____
_____
_____
_____

What did I feel today? _____
_____
_____
_____

What am I grateful for today? _____
_____
_____
_____

What challenged me today? _____
_____
_____
_____

How can I overcome that challenge? _____
_____
_____
_____

What did I savor today? _____
_____
_____
_____

BUILDING _the_ BEST YOU THERE IS

_____ Date

What did I do today? _____
_____
_____
_____

What did I feel today? _____
_____
_____
_____

What am I grateful for today? _____
_____
_____
_____

What challenged me today? _____
_____
_____
_____

How can I overcome that challenge? _____
_____
_____
_____

What did I savor today? _____
_____
_____
_____

YEAR ONE

_____ Date

What did I do today? _____
_____
_____
_____

What did I feel today? _____
_____
_____
_____

What am I grateful for today? _____
_____
_____
_____

What challenged me today? _____
_____
_____
_____

How can I overcome that challenge? _____
_____
_____
_____

What did I savor today? _____
_____
_____
_____

YEAR TWO

BUILDING *the* BEST YOU THERE IS

What did I do today? _____

What did I do today? _____

What did I feel today? _____

What did I feel today? _____

What am I grateful for today? _____

What am I grateful for today? _____

What challenged me today? _____

What challenged me today? _____

How can I overcome that challenge? _____

How can I overcome that challenge? _____

What did I savor today? _____

What did I savor today? _____

YEAR ONE

YEAR TWO

BUILDING *the* BEST YOU THERE IS

What did I do today? _____   What did I do today? _____

_____   _____

_____   _____

_____   _____

What did I feel today? _____   What did I feel today? _____

_____   _____

_____   _____

What am I grateful for today? _____   What am I grateful for today? _____

_____   _____

_____   _____

What challenged me today? _____   What challenged me today? _____

_____   _____

_____   _____

How can I overcome that challenge? ___ How can I overcome that challenge? ___

_____   _____

_____   _____

What did I savor today? _____   What did I savor today? _____

_____   _____

_____   _____

_____ Date

What did I do today? _____

_____
_____
_____
_____

What did I feel today? _____

_____
_____
_____
_____

What am I grateful for today? _____

_____
_____
_____
_____

What challenged me today? _____

_____
_____
_____
_____

How can I overcome that challenge? _____

_____
_____
_____
_____

What did I savor today? _____

_____
_____
_____
_____

YEAR ONE

_____ Date

What did I do today? _____

_____
_____
_____
_____

What did I feel today? _____

_____
_____
_____
_____

What am I grateful for today? _____

_____
_____
_____
_____

What challenged me today? _____

_____
_____
_____
_____

How can I overcome that challenge? _____

_____
_____
_____
_____

What did I savor today? _____

_____
_____
_____
_____

YEAR TWO

BUILDING *the* BEST YOU THERE IS

_____ Date   _____ Date

What did I do today? _____   *What did I do today?* _____
_____   _____
_____   _____
_____   _____

What did I feel today? _____   *What did I feel today?* _____
_____   _____
_____   _____
_____   _____

What am I grateful for today? _____   *What am I grateful for today?* _____
_____   _____
_____   _____
_____   _____

What challenged me today? _____   *What challenged me today?* _____
_____   _____
_____   _____
_____   _____

How can I overcome that challenge? ___   *How can I overcome that challenge?* ___
_____   _____
_____   _____
_____   _____

What did I savor today? _____   *What did I savor today?* _____
_____   _____
_____   _____
_____   _____

YEAR ONE   YEAR TWO

BUILDING *the* BEST YOU THERE IS

_____ Date   _____ Date

What did I do today? _____   What did I do today? _____

_____   _____
_____   _____
_____   _____

What did I feel today? _____   What did I feel today? _____

_____   _____
_____   _____
_____   _____

What am I grateful for today? _____   What am I grateful for today? _____

_____   _____
_____   _____
_____   _____

What challenged me today? _____   What challenged me today? _____

_____   _____
_____   _____
_____   _____

How can I overcome that challenge? _____   How can I overcome that challenge? _____

_____   _____
_____   _____
_____   _____

What did I savor today? _____   What did I savor today? _____

_____   _____
_____   _____
_____   _____

YEAR ONE   YEAR TWO

BUILDING *the* BEST YOU THERE IS

What did I do today? _____   What did I do today? _____

_____   _____

_____   _____

_____   _____

What did I feel today? _____   What did I feel today? _____

_____   _____

_____   _____

_____   _____

What am I grateful for today? _____   What am I grateful for today? _____

_____   _____

_____   _____

_____   _____

What challenged me today? _____   What challenged me today? _____

_____   _____

_____   _____

_____   _____

How can I overcome that challenge? ___   How can I overcome that challenge? ___

_____   _____

_____   _____

_____   _____

What did I savor today? _____   What did I savor today? _____

_____   _____

_____   _____

_____   _____

BUILDING *the* BEST YOU THERE IS

_____ Date

What did I do today? _____
_____
_____
_____
_____

What did I feel today? _____
_____
_____
_____

What am I grateful for today? _____
_____
_____
_____

What challenged me today? _____
_____
_____
_____
_____

How can I overcome that challenge? _____
_____
_____
_____

What did I savor today? _____
_____
_____
_____

YEAR ONE

_____ Date

What did I do today? _____
_____
_____
_____
_____

What did I feel today? _____
_____
_____
_____

What am I grateful for today? _____
_____
_____
_____

What challenged me today? _____
_____
_____
_____
_____

How can I overcome that challenge? _____
_____
_____
_____

What did I savor today? _____
_____
_____
_____

YEAR TWO

BUILDING _the_ BEST YOU THERE IS

_____ Date

What did I do today? _____

_____
_____
_____
_____

What did I feel today? _____

_____
_____
_____

What am I grateful for today? _____

_____
_____
_____

What challenged me today? _____

_____
_____
_____

How can I overcome that challenge? _____

_____
_____
_____

What did I savor today? _____

_____
_____
_____

YEAR ONE

_____ Date

What did I do today? _____

_____
_____
_____
_____

What did I feel today? _____

_____
_____
_____

What am I grateful for today? _____

_____
_____
_____

What challenged me today? _____

_____
_____
_____

How can I overcome that challenge? _____

_____
_____
_____

What did I savor today? _____

_____
_____
_____

YEAR TWO

BUILDING *the* BEST YOU THERE IS

	Date			Date

What did I do today? _____

_____

_____

_____

What did I feel today? _____

_____

_____

_____

What am I grateful for today? _____

_____

_____

_____

What challenged me today? _____

_____

_____

_____

How can I overcome that challenge? _____

_____

_____

_____

What did I savor today? _____

_____

_____

_____

What did I do today? _____

_____

_____

_____

What did I feel today? _____

_____

_____

_____

What am I grateful for today? _____

_____

_____

_____

What challenged me today? _____

_____

_____

_____

How can I overcome that challenge? _____

_____

_____

_____

What did I savor today? _____

_____

_____

_____

YEAR ONE   YEAR TWO

BUILDING *the* BEST YOU THERE IS

_____ Date

What did I do today? _____
_____
_____
_____

What did I feel today? _____
_____
_____
_____

What am I grateful for today? _____
_____
_____
_____

What challenged me today? _____
_____
_____
_____

How can I overcome that challenge? __
_____
_____
_____

What did I savor today? _____
_____
_____
_____

_____ Date

What did I do today? _____
_____
_____
_____

What did I feel today? _____
_____
_____
_____

What am I grateful for today? _____
_____
_____
_____

What challenged me today? _____
_____
_____
_____

How can I overcome that challenge? __
_____
_____
_____

What did I savor today? _____
_____
_____
_____

BUILDING _the_ BEST YOU THERE IS

_____ _Date_

What did I do today? _____

_____
_____
_____
_____

What did I feel today? _____

_____
_____
_____
_____

What am I grateful for today? _____

_____
_____
_____
_____

What challenged me today? _____

_____
_____
_____
_____

How can I overcome that challenge? _____

_____
_____
_____
_____

What did I savor today? _____

_____
_____
_____
_____

YEAR ONE

_____ _Date_

What did I do today? _____

_____
_____
_____
_____

What did I feel today? _____

_____
_____
_____
_____

What am I grateful for today? _____

_____
_____
_____
_____

What challenged me today? _____

_____
_____
_____
_____

How can I overcome that challenge? _____

_____
_____
_____
_____

What did I savor today? _____

_____
_____
_____
_____

YEAR TWO

BUILDING _the_ BEST YOU THERE IS

_____ Date   _____ Date

What did I do today? _____   *What did I do today?* _____
_____   _____
_____   _____
_____   _____

What did I feel today? _____   *What did I feel today?* _____
_____   _____
_____   _____
_____   _____

What am I grateful for today? _____   *What am I grateful for today?* _____
_____   _____
_____   _____
_____   _____

What challenged me today? _____   *What challenged me today?* _____
_____   _____
_____   _____
_____   _____

How can I overcome that challenge? __   *How can I overcome that challenge?* __
_____   _____
_____   _____
_____   _____

What did I savor today? _____   *What did I savor today?* _____
_____   _____
_____   _____
_____   _____

BUILDING *the* BEST YOU THERE IS

_____ Date

_____ Date

What did I do today? _____

What did I do today? _____

_____

_____

_____

_____

_____

_____

What did I feel today? _____

What did I feel today? _____

_____

_____

_____

_____

_____

_____

What am I grateful for today? _____

What am I grateful for today? _____

_____

_____

_____

_____

_____

_____

What challenged me today? _____

What challenged me today? _____

_____

_____

_____

_____

_____

_____

How can I overcome that challenge? _____

How can I overcome that challenge? _____

_____

_____

_____

_____

_____

_____

What did I savor today? _____

What did I savor today? _____

_____

_____

_____

_____

_____

_____

YEAR ONE

YEAR TWO

BUILDING *the* BEST YOU THERE IS

What did I do today?

What did I do today?

What did I feel today?

What did I feel today?

What am I grateful for today?

What am I grateful for today?

What challenged me today?

What challenged me today?

How can I overcome that challenge?

How can I overcome that challenge?

What did I savor today?

What did I savor today?

BUILDING *the* BEST YOU THERE IS

_____ Date

What did I do today? _____
_____
_____
_____
_____

What did I feel today? _____
_____
_____
_____
_____

What am I grateful for today? _____
_____
_____
_____
_____

What challenged me today? _____
_____
_____
_____
_____

How can I overcome that challenge? _____
_____
_____
_____
_____

What did I savor today? _____
_____
_____
_____
_____

YEAR ONE

_____ Date

What did I do today? _____
_____
_____
_____
_____

What did I feel today? _____
_____
_____
_____
_____

What am I grateful for today? _____
_____
_____
_____
_____

What challenged me today? _____
_____
_____
_____
_____

How can I overcome that challenge? _____
_____
_____
_____
_____

What did I savor today? _____
_____
_____
_____
_____

YEAR TWO

_____ Date

What did I do today? _____
_____
_____
_____
_____

What did I feel today? _____
_____
_____
_____

What am I grateful for today? _____
_____
_____
_____
_____

What challenged me today? _____
_____
_____
_____

How can I overcome that challenge? _____
_____
_____
_____

What did I savor today? _____
_____
_____
_____

_____ Date

What did I do today? _____
_____
_____
_____
_____

What did I feel today? _____
_____
_____
_____

What am I grateful for today? _____
_____
_____
_____
_____

What challenged me today? _____
_____
_____
_____

How can I overcome that challenge? _____
_____
_____
_____

What did I savor today? _____
_____
_____
_____

YEAR ONE

YEAR TWO

BUILDING *the* BEST YOU THERE IS

What did I do today? _____

_____
_____
_____
_____

What did I feel today? _____

_____
_____
_____

What am I grateful for today? _____

_____
_____
_____

What challenged me today? _____

_____
_____
_____

How can I overcome that challenge? _____

_____
_____
_____

What did I savor today? _____

_____
_____
_____

What did I do today? _____

_____
_____
_____
_____

What did I feel today? _____

_____
_____
_____

What am I grateful for today? _____

_____
_____
_____

What challenged me today? _____

_____
_____
_____

How can I overcome that challenge? _____

_____
_____
_____

What did I savor today? _____

_____
_____
_____

YEAR ONE

YEAR TWO

BUILDING *the* BEST YOU THERE IS

_____ Date

What did I do today? _____
_____
_____
_____

What did I feel today? _____
_____
_____
_____

What am I grateful for today? _____
_____
_____
_____

What challenged me today? _____
_____
_____
_____

How can I overcome that challenge? _____
_____
_____
_____

What did I savor today? _____
_____
_____
_____

YEAR ONE

_____ Date

What did I do today? _____
_____
_____
_____

What did I feel today? _____
_____
_____
_____

What am I grateful for today? _____
_____
_____
_____

What challenged me today? _____
_____
_____
_____

How can I overcome that challenge? _____
_____
_____
_____

What did I savor today? _____
_____
_____
_____

YEAR TWO

BUILDING the BEST YOU THERE IS

What did I do today?   What did I do today?

_____   _____
_____   _____
_____   _____
_____   _____

What did I feel today?   What did I feel today?

_____   _____
_____   _____
_____   _____
_____   _____

What am I grateful for today?   What am I grateful for today?

_____   _____
_____   _____
_____   _____
_____   _____

What challenged me today?   What challenged me today?

_____   _____
_____   _____
_____   _____
_____   _____

How can I overcome that challenge?   How can I overcome that challenge?

_____   _____
_____   _____
_____   _____
_____   _____

What did I savor today?   What did I savor today?

_____   _____
_____   _____
_____   _____
_____   _____

_____ Date

What did I do today? _____

_____

_____

_____

What did I feel today? _____

_____

_____

_____

What am I grateful for today? _____

_____

_____

_____

What challenged me today? _____

_____

_____

_____

How can I overcome that challenge? _____

_____

_____

_____

What did I savor today? _____

_____

_____

_____

_____ Date

What did I do today? _____

_____

_____

_____

What did I feel today? _____

_____

_____

_____

What am I grateful for today? _____

_____

_____

_____

What challenged me today? _____

_____

_____

_____

How can I overcome that challenge? _____

_____

_____

_____

What did I savor today? _____

_____

_____

_____

YEAR ONE

YEAR TWO

BUILDING *the* BEST YOU THERE IS

What did I do today? _____

_____

_____

_____

_____

What did I feel today? _____

_____

_____

_____

_____

What am I grateful for today? _____

_____

_____

_____

_____

What challenged me today? _____

_____

_____

_____

_____

How can I overcome that challenge? _____

_____

_____

_____

_____

What did I savor today? _____

_____

_____

_____

_____

YEAR ONE

What did I do today? _____

_____

_____

_____

_____

What did I feel today? _____

_____

_____

_____

_____

What am I grateful for today? _____

_____

_____

_____

_____

What challenged me today? _____

_____

_____

_____

_____

How can I overcome that challenge? _____

_____

_____

_____

_____

What did I savor today? _____

_____

_____

_____

_____

YEAR TWO

_____ Date   _____ Date

What did I do today? _____   What did I do today? _____
_____   _____
_____   _____
_____   _____

What did I feel today? _____   What did I feel today? _____
_____   _____
_____   _____
_____   _____

What am I grateful for today? _____   What am I grateful for today? _____
_____   _____
_____   _____
_____   _____

What challenged me today? _____   What challenged me today? _____
_____   _____
_____   _____
_____   _____

How can I overcome that challenge? _____   How can I overcome that challenge? _____
_____   _____
_____   _____
_____   _____

What did I savor today? _____   What did I savor today? _____
_____   _____
_____   _____
_____   _____

YEAR ONE   YEAR TWO

BUILDING _the_ BEST YOU THERE IS

What did I do today? _____

_____

_____

_____

What did I feel today? _____

_____

_____

_____

What am I grateful for today? _____

_____

_____

What challenged me today? _____

_____

_____

_____

How can I overcome that challenge? _____

_____

_____

_____

What did I savor today? _____

_____

_____

_____

What did I do today? _____

_____

_____

_____

What did I feel today? _____

_____

_____

_____

What am I grateful for today? _____

_____

_____

What challenged me today? _____

_____

_____

_____

How can I overcome that challenge? _____

_____

_____

_____

What did I savor today? _____

_____

_____

_____

YEAR ONE

YEAR TWO

_____ Date   _____ Date

What did I do today? _____   What did I do today? _____
_____   _____
_____   _____
_____   _____

What did I feel today? _____   What did I feel today? _____
_____   _____
_____   _____
_____   _____

What am I grateful for today? _____   What am I grateful for today? _____
_____   _____
_____   _____
_____   _____

What challenged me today? _____   What challenged me today? _____
_____   _____
_____   _____
_____   _____

How can I overcome that challenge? _____   How can I overcome that challenge? _____
_____   _____
_____   _____
_____   _____

What did I savor today? _____   What did I savor today? _____
_____   _____
_____   _____
_____   _____

YEAR ONE   YEAR TWO

BUILDING _the_ BEST YOU THERE IS

_____ Date   _____ Date

What did I do today? _____   *What did I do today?* _____

_____   _____
_____   _____
_____   _____
_____   _____

What did I feel today? _____   *What did I feel today?* _____

_____   _____
_____   _____
_____   _____
_____   _____

What am I grateful for today? _____   *What am I grateful for today?* _____

_____   _____
_____   _____
_____   _____
_____   _____

What challenged me today? _____   *What challenged me today?* _____

_____   _____
_____   _____
_____   _____
_____   _____

How can I overcome that challenge? _____   *How can I overcome that challenge?* _____

_____   _____
_____   _____
_____   _____
_____   _____

What did I savor today? _____   *What did I savor today?* _____

_____   _____
_____   _____
_____   _____
_____   _____

YEAR ONE   YEAR TWO

BUILDING *the* BEST YOU THERE IS

_____ Date

What did I do today? _____
_____
_____
_____

What did I feel today? _____
_____
_____
_____

What am I grateful for today? _____
_____
_____
_____

What challenged me today? _____
_____
_____
_____

How can I overcome that challenge? _____
_____
_____
_____

What did I savor today? _____
_____
_____
_____

YEAR ONE

_____ Date

What did I do today? _____
_____
_____
_____

What did I feel today? _____
_____
_____
_____

What am I grateful for today? _____
_____
_____
_____

What challenged me today? _____
_____
_____
_____

How can I overcome that challenge? _____
_____
_____
_____

What did I savor today? _____
_____
_____
_____

YEAR TWO

BUILDING _the_ BEST YOU THERE IS

Date		Date

What did I do today? _____

What did I feel today? _____

What am I grateful for today? _____

What challenged me today? _____

How can I overcome that challenge? _____

What did I savor today? _____

What did I do today? _____

What did I feel today? _____

What am I grateful for today? _____

What challenged me today? _____

How can I overcome that challenge? _____

What did I savor today? _____

YEAR TWO

BUILDING *the* BEST YOU THERE IS

_____ Date   _____ Date

What did I do today? _____   What did I do today? _____
_____   _____
_____   _____
_____   _____
_____   _____

What did I feel today? _____   What did I feel today? _____
_____   _____
_____   _____
_____   _____
_____   _____

What am I grateful for today? _____   What am I grateful for today? _____
_____   _____
_____   _____
_____   _____
_____   _____

What challenged me today? _____   What challenged me today? _____
_____   _____
_____   _____
_____   _____

How can I overcome that challenge? ___   How can I overcome that challenge? ___
_____   _____
_____   _____
_____   _____
_____   _____

What did I savor today? _____   What did I savor today? _____
_____   _____
_____   _____
_____   _____

BUILDING _the_ BEST YOU THERE IS

What did I do today? _____

What did I do today? _____

_____

_____

_____

_____

_____

_____

_____

_____

What did I feel today? _____

What did I feel today? _____

_____

_____

_____

_____

_____

_____

What am I grateful for today? _____

What am I grateful for today? _____

_____

_____

_____

_____

_____

_____

_____

_____

What challenged me today? _____

What challenged me today? _____

_____

_____

_____

_____

_____

_____

_____

_____

How can I overcome that challenge? _____

How can I overcome that challenge? _____

_____

_____

_____

_____

_____

_____

What did I savor today? _____

What did I savor today? _____

_____

_____

_____

_____

_____

_____

YEAR ONE

YEAR TWO

BUILDING *the* BEST YOU THERE IS

_____ Date   _____ Date

What did I do today? _____   What did I do today? _____
_____   _____
_____   _____
_____   _____

What did I feel today? _____   What did I feel today? _____
_____   _____
_____   _____
_____   _____

What am I grateful for today? _____   What am I grateful for today? _____
_____   _____
_____   _____
_____   _____

What challenged me today? _____   What challenged me today? _____
_____   _____
_____   _____
_____   _____

How can I overcome that challenge? __   How can I overcome that challenge? __
_____   _____
_____   _____
_____   _____

What did I savor today? _____   What did I savor today? _____
_____   _____
_____   _____
_____   _____

BUILDING _the_ BEST YOU THERE IS

What did I do today? _____

_____
_____
_____

What did I feel today? _____

_____
_____
_____

What am I grateful for today? _____

_____
_____
_____

What challenged me today? _____

_____
_____
_____

How can I overcome that challenge? _____

_____
_____
_____

What did I savor today? _____

_____
_____
_____

What did I do today? _____

_____
_____
_____

What did I feel today? _____

_____
_____
_____

What am I grateful for today? _____

_____
_____
_____

What challenged me today? _____

_____
_____
_____

How can I overcome that challenge? _____

_____
_____
_____

What did I savor today? _____

_____
_____
_____

YEAR ONE

YEAR TWO

BUILDING *the* BEST YOU THERE IS

_____ Date

What did I do today? _____
_____
_____
_____
_____

What did I feel today? _____
_____
_____
_____

What am I grateful for today? _____
_____
_____
_____

What challenged me today? _____
_____
_____
_____

How can I overcome that challenge? _____
_____
_____
_____

What did I savor today? _____
_____
_____
_____

YEAR ONE

_____ Date

What did I do today? _____
_____
_____
_____
_____

What did I feel today? _____
_____
_____
_____

What am I grateful for today? _____
_____
_____
_____

What challenged me today? _____
_____
_____
_____

How can I overcome that challenge? _____
_____
_____
_____

What did I savor today? _____
_____
_____
_____

YEAR TWO

_____ Date

What did I do today? _____

_____
_____
_____

What did I feel today? _____

_____
_____
_____

What am I grateful for today? _____

_____
_____
_____

What challenged me today? _____

_____
_____
_____

How can I overcome that challenge? _____

_____
_____
_____

What did I savor today? _____

_____
_____
_____

YEAR ONE

_____ Date

What did I do today? _____

_____
_____
_____

What did I feel today? _____

_____
_____
_____

What am I grateful for today? _____

_____
_____
_____

What challenged me today? _____

_____
_____
_____

How can I overcome that challenge? _____

_____
_____
_____

What did I savor today? _____

_____
_____
_____

YEAR TWO

BUILDING _the_ BEST YOU THERE IS

What did I do today? _____

_____
_____
_____
_____

What did I feel today? _____

_____
_____
_____

What am I grateful for today? _____

_____
_____
_____
_____

What challenged me today? _____

_____
_____
_____

How can I overcome that challenge? _____

_____
_____
_____

What did I savor today? _____

_____
_____
_____

What did I do today? _____

_____
_____
_____
_____

What did I feel today? _____

_____
_____
_____

What am I grateful for today? _____

_____
_____
_____
_____

What challenged me today? _____

_____
_____
_____

How can I overcome that challenge? _____

_____
_____
_____

What did I savor today? _____

_____
_____
_____

YEAR ONE

YEAR TWO

BUILDING the BEST YOU THERE IS

What did I do today? _____

What did I do today? _____

_____

_____

_____

_____

_____

_____

What did I feel today? _____

What did I feel today? _____

_____

_____

_____

_____

_____

_____

What am I grateful for today? _____

What am I grateful for today? _____

_____

_____

_____

_____

_____

_____

What challenged me today? _____

What challenged me today? _____

_____

_____

_____

_____

_____

_____

How can I overcome that challenge? _____

How can I overcome that challenge? _____

_____

_____

_____

_____

_____

_____

What did I savor today? _____

What did I savor today? _____

_____

_____

_____

_____

_____

_____

_____ Date   _____ Date

What did I do today? _____   What did I do today? _____

_____   _____

_____   _____

_____   _____

What did I feel today? _____   What did I feel today? _____

_____   _____

_____   _____

_____   _____

What am I grateful for today? _____   What am I grateful for today? _____

_____   _____

_____   _____

_____   _____

What challenged me today? _____   What challenged me today? _____

_____   _____

_____   _____

_____   _____

How can I overcome that challenge? _____ How can I overcome that challenge? _____

_____   _____

_____   _____

_____   _____

What did I savor today? _____   What did I savor today? _____

_____   _____

_____   _____

_____   _____

_____ Date   _____ Date

What did I do today? _____   What did I do today? _____
_____   _____
_____   _____
_____   _____
_____   _____

What did I feel today? _____   What did I feel today? _____
_____   _____
_____   _____
_____   _____
_____   _____

What am I grateful for today? _____   What am I grateful for today? _____
_____   _____
_____   _____
_____   _____
_____   _____

What challenged me today? _____   What challenged me today? _____
_____   _____
_____   _____
_____   _____
_____   _____

How can I overcome that challenge? ____   How can I overcome that challenge? ____
_____   _____
_____   _____
_____   _____
_____   _____

What did I savor today? _____   What did I savor today? _____
_____   _____
_____   _____
_____   _____
_____   _____

YEAR ONE   YEAR TWO

BUILDING *the* BEST YOU THERE IS

_____ *Date*

What did I do today? _____

_____
_____
_____

What did I feel today? _____

_____
_____
_____

What am I grateful for today? _____

_____
_____
_____

What challenged me today? _____

_____
_____
_____

How can I overcome that challenge? _____

_____
_____
_____

What did I savor today? _____

_____
_____
_____

YEAR ONE

_____ *Date*

What did I do today? _____

_____
_____
_____

What did I feel today? _____

_____
_____
_____

What am I grateful for today? _____

_____
_____
_____

What challenged me today? _____

_____
_____
_____

How can I overcome that challenge? _____

_____
_____
_____

What did I savor today? _____

_____
_____
_____

YEAR TWO

BUILDING *the* BEST YOU THERE IS

What do I value most in life? _____

_____

_____

_____

_____

Am I influenced by material things? _____

_____

_____

_____

_____

Do I treasure family? _____

_____

_____

_____

_____

What do I admire most about others? _____

_____

_____

_____

_____

How do I picture myself in twenty years? _____

_____

_____

_____

_____

How do I get there? _____

_____

_____

_____

_____

Am I bound to the past?

Do I repeat old patterns?

Do I long for a new direction?

What is that direction?

How do I get there?

What's my first step to take?

What do I value most in life? _____
_____
_____
_____
_____

Am I influenced by material things? _____
_____
_____
_____
_____

Do I treasure family? _____
_____
_____
_____
_____

What do I admire most about others? _____
_____
_____
_____
_____

How do I picture myself in twenty years? _____
_____
_____
_____
_____

How do I get there? _____
_____
_____
_____
_____

Am I bound to the past? _____
_____
_____
_____
_____

Do I repeat old patterns? _____
_____
_____
_____
_____

Do I long for a new direction? _____
_____
_____
_____

What is that direction? _____
_____
_____
_____

How do I get there? _____
_____
_____
_____

What's my first step to take? _____
_____
_____
_____

BUILDING *the* BEST YOU THERE IS

What did I do today? _____

_____

_____

_____

_____

What did I feel today? _____

_____

_____

_____

What am I grateful for today? _____

_____

_____

_____

What challenged me today? _____

_____

_____

_____

How can I overcome that challenge? ___

_____

_____

_____

What did I savor today? _____

_____

_____

_____

YEAR ONE

What did I do today? _____

_____

_____

_____

_____

What did I feel today? _____

_____

_____

_____

What am I grateful for today? _____

_____

_____

_____

What challenged me today? _____

_____

_____

_____

How can I overcome that challenge? ___

_____

_____

_____

What did I savor today? _____

_____

_____

_____

YEAR TWO

BUILDING *the* BEST YOU THERE IS

_____ Date   _____ Date

What did I do today? _____ What did I do today? _____

_____ _____

_____ _____

_____ _____

What did I feel today? _____ What did I feel today? _____

_____ _____

_____ _____

_____ _____

What am I grateful for today? _____ What am I grateful for today? _____

_____ _____

_____ _____

_____ _____

What challenged me today? _____ What challenged me today? _____

_____ _____

_____ _____

_____ _____

How can I overcome that challenge? _____ How can I overcome that challenge? _____

_____ _____

_____ _____

_____ _____

What did I savor today? _____ What did I savor today? _____

_____ _____

_____ _____

_____ _____

YEAR ONE   YEAR TWO

BUILDING _the_ BEST YOU THERE IS

_____ Date

What did I do today? _____
_____
_____
_____
_____

What did I feel today? _____
_____
_____
_____
_____

What am I grateful for today? _____
_____
_____
_____
_____

What challenged me today? _____
_____
_____
_____
_____

How can I overcome that challenge? _____
_____
_____
_____
_____

What did I savor today? _____
_____
_____
_____
_____

YEAR ONE

_____ Date

What did I do today? _____
_____
_____
_____
_____

What did I feel today? _____
_____
_____
_____
_____

What am I grateful for today? _____
_____
_____
_____
_____

What challenged me today? _____
_____
_____
_____
_____

How can I overcome that challenge? _____
_____
_____
_____
_____

What did I savor today? _____
_____
_____
_____
_____

YEAR TWO

BUILDING *the* BEST YOU THERE IS

_____ Date

What did I do today? _____
_____
_____
_____

What did I feel today? _____
_____
_____
_____

What am I grateful for today? _____
_____
_____
_____

What challenged me today? _____
_____
_____
_____

How can I overcome that challenge? _____
_____
_____
_____

What did I savor today? _____
_____
_____
_____

_____ Date

What did I do today? _____
_____
_____
_____

What did I feel today? _____
_____
_____
_____

What am I grateful for today? _____
_____
_____
_____

What challenged me today? _____
_____
_____
_____

How can I overcome that challenge? _____
_____
_____
_____

What did I savor today? _____
_____
_____
_____

YEAR ONE   YEAR TWO

BUILDING _the_ BEST YOU THERE IS

What did I do today? ———

_____
_____
_____
_____

What did I feel today? ———

_____
_____
_____
_____

What am I grateful for today? ———

_____
_____
_____
_____

What challenged me today? ———

_____
_____
_____
_____

How can I overcome that challenge? ———

_____
_____
_____
_____

What did I savor today? ———

_____
_____
_____
_____

What did I do today? ———

_____
_____
_____
_____

What did I feel today? ———

_____
_____
_____
_____

What am I grateful for today? ———

_____
_____
_____
_____

What challenged me today? ———

_____
_____
_____
_____

How can I overcome that challenge? ———

_____
_____
_____
_____

What did I savor today? ———

_____
_____
_____
_____

YEAR ONE   YEAR TWO

BUILDING _the_ BEST YOU THERE IS

What did I do today? _____   What did I do today? _____

_____   _____

_____   _____

_____   _____

What did I feel today? _____   What did I feel today? _____

_____   _____

_____   _____

_____   _____

What am I grateful for today? _____   What am I grateful for today? _____

_____   _____

_____   _____

_____   _____

What challenged me today? _____   What challenged me today? _____

_____   _____

_____   _____

_____   _____

How can I overcome that challenge? ___   How can I overcome that challenge? ___

_____   _____

_____   _____

_____   _____

What did I savor today? _____   What did I savor today? _____

_____   _____

_____   _____

_____   _____

What did I do today? _____

_____
_____
_____
_____

What did I feel today? _____

_____
_____
_____
_____

What am I grateful for today? _____

_____
_____
_____
_____

What challenged me today? _____

_____
_____
_____
_____

How can I overcome that challenge? _____

_____
_____
_____
_____

What did I savor today? _____

_____
_____
_____
_____

What did I do today? _____

_____
_____
_____
_____

What did I feel today? _____

_____
_____
_____
_____

What am I grateful for today? _____

_____
_____
_____
_____

What challenged me today? _____

_____
_____
_____
_____

How can I overcome that challenge? _____

_____
_____
_____
_____

What did I savor today? _____

_____
_____
_____
_____

YEAR ONE   YEAR TWO

BUILDING *the* BEST YOU THERE IS

What did I do today?

_____

_____

_____

What did I feel today?

_____

_____

_____

What am I grateful for today?

_____

_____

_____

What challenged me today?

_____

_____

_____

How can I overcome that challenge?

_____

_____

_____

What did I savor today?

_____

_____

_____

What did I do today?

_____

_____

_____

What did I feel today?

_____

_____

_____

What am I grateful for today?

_____

_____

_____

What challenged me today?

_____

_____

_____

How can I overcome that challenge?

_____

_____

_____

What did I savor today?

_____

_____

_____

YEAR ONE

YEAR TWO

BUILDING *the* BEST YOU THERE IS

_____ Date | _____ Date

What did I do today? _____ | *What did I do today?* _____

_____ | _____
_____ | _____
_____ | _____
_____ | _____

What did I feel today? _____ | *What did I feel today?* _____

_____ | _____
_____ | _____
_____ | _____
_____ | _____

What am I grateful for today? _____ | *What am I grateful for today?* _____

_____ | _____
_____ | _____
_____ | _____
_____ | _____

What challenged me today? _____ | *What challenged me today?* _____

_____ | _____
_____ | _____
_____ | _____
_____ | _____

How can I overcome that challenge? _____ | *How can I overcome that challenge?* _____

_____ | _____
_____ | _____
_____ | _____
_____ | _____

What did I savor today? _____ | *What did I savor today?* _____

_____ | _____
_____ | _____
_____ | _____
_____ | _____

YEAR ONE | YEAR TWO

BUILDING *the* BEST YOU THERE IS

_____ Date   _____ Date

What did I do today? _____   *What did I do today?* _____
_____   _____
_____   _____
_____   _____

What did I feel today? _____   *What did I feel today?* _____
_____   _____
_____   _____
_____   _____

What am I grateful for today? _____   *What am I grateful for today?* _____
_____   _____
_____   _____
_____   _____

What challenged me today? _____   *What challenged me today?* _____
_____   _____
_____   _____
_____   _____

How can I overcome that challenge? _____   *How can I overcome that challenge?* _____
_____   _____
_____   _____
_____   _____

What did I savor today? _____   *What did I savor today?* _____
_____   _____
_____   _____
_____   _____

YEAR ONE   YEAR TWO

BUILDING *the* BEST YOU THERE IS

What did I do today? _____

_____

_____

_____

What did I do today? _____

_____

_____

_____

What did I feel today? _____

_____

_____

_____

What did I feel today? _____

_____

_____

_____

What am I grateful for today? _____

_____

_____

_____

What am I grateful for today? _____

_____

_____

_____

What challenged me today? _____

_____

_____

_____

What challenged me today? _____

_____

_____

_____

How can I overcome that challenge? _____

_____

_____

_____

How can I overcome that challenge? _____

_____

_____

_____

What did I savor today? _____

_____

_____

_____

_____

What did I savor today? _____

_____

_____

_____

_____

BUILDING *the* BEST YOU THERE IS

_____ Date

What did I do today? _____
_____
_____
_____
_____

What did I feel today? _____
_____
_____
_____
_____

What am I grateful for today? _____
_____
_____
_____
_____

What challenged me today? _____
_____
_____
_____
_____

How can I overcome that challenge? _____
_____
_____
_____
_____

What did I savor today? _____
_____
_____
_____
_____

YEAR ONE

_____ Date

What did I do today? _____
_____
_____
_____
_____

What did I feel today? _____
_____
_____
_____
_____

What am I grateful for today? _____
_____
_____
_____
_____

What challenged me today? _____
_____
_____
_____
_____

How can I overcome that challenge? _____
_____
_____
_____
_____

What did I savor today? _____
_____
_____
_____
_____

YEAR TWO

BUILDING the BEST YOU THERE IS

Date _____

What did I do today? _____
_____
_____
_____

What did I feel today? _____
_____
_____
_____

What am I grateful for today? _____
_____
_____
_____

What challenged me today? _____
_____
_____
_____

How can I overcome that challenge? _____
_____
_____
_____

What did I savor today? _____
_____
_____
_____

YEAR ONE

Date _____

What did I do today? _____
_____
_____
_____

What did I feel today? _____
_____
_____
_____

What am I grateful for today? _____
_____
_____
_____

What challenged me today? _____
_____
_____
_____

How can I overcome that challenge? _____
_____
_____
_____

What did I savor today? _____
_____
_____
_____

YEAR TWO

BUILDING _the_ BEST YOU THERE IS

_____ Date

What did I do today? _____
_____
_____
_____

What did I feel today? _____
_____
_____
_____

What am I grateful for today? _____
_____
_____
_____

What challenged me today? _____
_____
_____
_____

How can I overcome that challenge? _____
_____
_____
_____

What did I savor today? _____
_____
_____
_____

_____ Date

What did I do today? _____
_____
_____
_____

What did I feel today? _____
_____
_____
_____

What am I grateful for today? _____
_____
_____
_____

What challenged me today? _____
_____
_____
_____

How can I overcome that challenge? _____
_____
_____
_____

What did I savor today? _____
_____
_____
_____

BUILDING the BEST YOU THERE IS

What did I do today? _____

_____
_____
_____
_____

What did I feel today? _____

_____
_____
_____
_____

What am I grateful for today? _____

_____
_____
_____
_____

What challenged me today? _____

_____
_____
_____
_____

How can I overcome that challenge? _____

_____
_____
_____
_____

What did I savor today? _____

_____
_____
_____
_____

What did I do today? _____

_____
_____
_____
_____

What did I feel today? _____

_____
_____
_____
_____

What am I grateful for today? _____

_____
_____
_____
_____

What challenged me today? _____

_____
_____
_____
_____

How can I overcome that challenge? _____

_____
_____
_____
_____

What did I savor today? _____

_____
_____
_____
_____

YEAR ONE

YEAR TWO

BUILDING *the* BEST YOU THERE IS

_____ Date

What did I do today? _____
_____
_____
_____

What did I feel today? _____
_____
_____
_____

What am I grateful for today? _____
_____
_____
_____

What challenged me today? _____
_____
_____
_____

How can I overcome that challenge? _____
_____
_____
_____

What did I savor today? _____
_____
_____
_____

YEAR ONE

_____ Date

What did I do today? _____
_____
_____
_____

What did I feel today? _____
_____
_____
_____

What am I grateful for today? _____
_____
_____
_____

What challenged me today? _____
_____
_____
_____

How can I overcome that challenge? _____
_____
_____
_____

What did I savor today? _____
_____
_____
_____

YEAR TWO

BUILDING _the_ BEST YOU THERE IS

_____ Date

What did I do today? _____
_____
_____
_____
_____

What did I feel today? _____
_____
_____
_____
_____

What am I grateful for today? _____
_____
_____
_____
_____

What challenged me today? _____
_____
_____
_____
_____

How can I overcome that challenge? _____
_____
_____
_____
_____

What did I savor today? _____
_____
_____
_____
_____

YEAR ONE

_____ Date

What did I do today? _____
_____
_____
_____
_____

What did I feel today? _____
_____
_____
_____
_____

What am I grateful for today? _____
_____
_____
_____
_____

What challenged me today? _____
_____
_____
_____
_____

How can I overcome that challenge? _____
_____
_____
_____
_____

What did I savor today? _____
_____
_____
_____
_____

YEAR TWO

What did I do today? _____   What did I do today? _____
_____   _____
_____   _____
_____   _____
_____   _____

What did I feel today? _____   What did I feel today? _____
_____   _____
_____   _____
_____   _____

What am I grateful for today? _____ What am I grateful for today? _____
_____   _____
_____   _____
_____   _____

What challenged me today?   What challenged me today?
_____   _____
_____   _____
_____   _____

How can I overcome that challenge? _____   How can I overcome that challenge? _____
_____   _____
_____   _____
_____   _____

What did I savor today? _____   What did I savor today? _____
_____   _____
_____   _____
_____   _____

BUILDING *the* BEST YOU THERE IS

_____ Date   _____ Date

What did I do today? _____   *What did I do today?* _____
_____   _____
_____   _____
_____   _____

What did I feel today? _____   *What did I feel today?* _____
_____   _____
_____   _____
_____   _____

What am I grateful for today? _____   *What am I grateful for today?* _____
_____   _____
_____   _____
_____   _____

What challenged me today? _____   *What challenged me today?* _____
_____   _____
_____   _____
_____   _____

How can I overcome that challenge? _____   *How can I overcome that challenge?* _____
_____   _____
_____   _____
_____   _____

What did I savor today? _____   *What did I savor today?* _____
_____   _____
_____   _____
_____   _____

YEAR ONE   YEAR TWO

BUILDING *the* BEST YOU THERE IS

_____ Date

What did I do today? _____
_____
_____
_____

What did I feel today? _____
_____
_____
_____

What am I grateful for today? _____
_____
_____
_____

What challenged me today? _____
_____
_____
_____

How can I overcome that challenge? _____
_____
_____
_____

What did I savor today? _____
_____
_____
_____

YEAR ONE

_____ Date

What did I do today? _____
_____
_____
_____

What did I feel today? _____
_____
_____
_____

What am I grateful for today? _____
_____
_____
_____

What challenged me today? _____
_____
_____
_____

How can I overcome that challenge? _____
_____
_____
_____

What did I savor today? _____
_____
_____
_____

YEAR TWO

BUILDING _the_ BEST YOU THERE IS

_____ Date

What did I do today? _____

_____

_____

_____

What did I feel today? _____

_____

_____

_____

What am I grateful for today? _____

_____

_____

_____

What challenged me today? _____

_____

_____

_____

How can I overcome that challenge? _____

_____

_____

_____

What did I savor today? _____

_____

_____

_____

YEAR ONE

_____ Date

What did I do today? _____

_____

_____

_____

What did I feel today? _____

_____

_____

_____

What am I grateful for today? _____

_____

_____

_____

What challenged me today? _____

_____

_____

_____

How can I overcome that challenge? _____

_____

_____

_____

What did I savor today? _____

_____

_____

_____

YEAR TWO

BUILDING *the* BEST YOU THERE IS

_____ Date

What did I do today? _____

_____

_____

_____

What did I feel today? _____

_____

_____

_____

What am I grateful for today? _____

_____

_____

_____

What challenged me today? _____

_____

_____

_____

How can I overcome that challenge? ___

_____

_____

_____

What did I savor today? _____

_____

_____

_____

_____ Date

What did I do today? _____

_____

_____

_____

What did I feel today? _____

_____

_____

_____

What am I grateful for today? _____

_____

_____

_____

What challenged me today? _____

_____

_____

_____

How can I overcome that challenge? ___

_____

_____

_____

What did I savor today? _____

_____

_____

_____

YEAR ONE   YEAR TWO

BUILDING *the* BEST YOU THERE IS

_____ Date   _____ Date

What did I do today? _____   What did I do today? _____

_____ _____

_____ _____

_____ _____

What did I feel today? _____   What did I feel today? _____

_____ _____

_____ _____

_____ _____

What am I grateful for today? _____ What am I grateful for today? _____

_____ _____

_____ _____

_____ _____

What challenged me today? _____ What challenged me today? _____

_____ _____

_____ _____

_____ _____

How can I overcome that challenge? _____ How can I overcome that challenge? _____

_____ _____

_____ _____

_____ _____

What did I savor today? _____ What did I savor today? _____

_____ _____

_____ _____

_____ _____

YEAR ONE   YEAR TWO

BUILDING _the_ BEST YOU THERE IS

What did I do today? _____

_____
_____
_____
_____

What did I feel today? _____

_____
_____
_____
_____

What am I grateful for today? _____

_____
_____
_____
_____

What challenged me today? _____

_____
_____
_____

How can I overcome that challenge? _____

_____
_____
_____
_____

What did I savor today? _____

_____
_____
_____
_____

What did I do today? _____

_____
_____
_____
_____

What did I feel today? _____

_____
_____
_____
_____

What am I grateful for today? _____

_____
_____
_____
_____

What challenged me today? _____

_____
_____
_____

How can I overcome that challenge? _____

_____
_____
_____
_____

What did I savor today? _____

_____
_____
_____
_____

YEAR ONE   YEAR TWO

BUILDING the BEST YOU THERE IS

_____ _Date_

What did I do today? _____

_____
_____
_____
_____

What did I feel today? _____

_____
_____
_____
_____

What am I grateful for today? _____

_____
_____
_____
_____

What challenged me today? _____

_____
_____
_____
_____

How can I overcome that challenge? _____

_____
_____
_____
_____

What did I savor today? _____

_____
_____
_____
_____

YEAR ONE

_____ _Date_

What did I do today? _____

_____
_____
_____
_____

What did I feel today? _____

_____
_____
_____
_____

What am I grateful for today? _____

_____
_____
_____
_____

What challenged me today? _____

_____
_____
_____
_____

How can I overcome that challenge? _____

_____
_____
_____
_____

What did I savor today? _____

_____
_____
_____
_____

YEAR TWO

BUILDING _the_ BEST YOU THERE IS

_____ Date

What did I do today? _____
_____
_____
_____
_____

What did I feel today? _____
_____
_____
_____

What am I grateful for today? _____
_____
_____
_____

What challenged me today? _____
_____
_____
_____

How can I overcome that challenge? _____
_____
_____
_____

What did I savor today? _____
_____
_____
_____

YEAR ONE

_____ Date

What did I do today? _____
_____
_____
_____
_____

What did I feel today? _____
_____
_____
_____

What am I grateful for today? _____
_____
_____
_____

What challenged me today? _____
_____
_____
_____

How can I overcome that challenge? _____
_____
_____
_____

What did I savor today? _____
_____
_____
_____

YEAR TWO

BUILDING _the_ BEST YOU THERE IS

_____ Date

_____ Date

What did I do today? _____

What did I do today? _____

What did I feel today? _____

What did I feel today? _____

What am I grateful for today? _____

What am I grateful for today? _____

What challenged me today? _____

What challenged me today? _____

How can I overcome that challenge? _____

How can I overcome that challenge? _____

What did I savor today? _____

What did I savor today? _____

BUILDING _the_ BEST YOU THERE IS

_____ Date

What did I do today? _____
_____
_____
_____

What did I feel today? _____
_____
_____
_____

What am I grateful for today? _____
_____
_____
_____

What challenged me today? _____
_____
_____
_____

How can I overcome that challenge? _____
_____
_____
_____

What did I savor today? _____
_____
_____
_____

YEAR ONE

_____ Date

What did I do today? _____
_____
_____
_____

What did I feel today? _____
_____
_____
_____

What am I grateful for today? _____
_____
_____
_____

What challenged me today? _____
_____
_____
_____

How can I overcome that challenge? _____
_____
_____
_____

What did I savor today? _____
_____
_____
_____

YEAR TWO

BUILDING *the* BEST YOU THERE IS

What did I do today? _____

_____
_____
_____
_____

What did I feel today? _____

_____
_____
_____
_____

What am I grateful for today? _____

_____
_____
_____
_____

What challenged me today? _____

_____
_____
_____
_____

How can I overcome that challenge? _____

_____
_____
_____
_____

What did I savor today? _____

_____
_____
_____
_____

YEAR ONE

What did I do today? _____

_____
_____
_____
_____

What did I feel today? _____

_____
_____
_____
_____

What am I grateful for today? _____

_____
_____
_____
_____

What challenged me today? _____

_____
_____
_____
_____

How can I overcome that challenge? _____

_____
_____
_____
_____

What did I savor today? _____

_____
_____
_____
_____

YEAR TWO

_____ Date   _____ Date

What did I do today? _____   *What did I do today?* _____
_____   _____
_____   _____
_____   _____

What did I feel today? _____   *What did I feel today?* _____
_____   _____
_____   _____
_____   _____

What am I grateful for today? _____   *What am I grateful for today?* _____
_____   _____
_____   _____
_____   _____

What challenged me today? _____   *What challenged me today?* _____
_____   _____
_____   _____
_____   _____

How can I overcome that challenge? _____   *How can I overcome that challenge?* _____
_____   _____
_____   _____
_____   _____

What did I savor today? _____   *What did I savor today?* _____
_____   _____
_____   _____
_____   _____

YEAR ONE   YEAR TWO

BUILDING *the* BEST YOU THERE IS

	Date	_Date_

What did I do today? _____

_____

_____

_____

_____

What did I feel today? _____

_____

_____

_____

_____

What am I grateful for today? _____

_____

_____

_____

_____

What challenged me today? _____

_____

_____

_____

_____

How can I overcome that challenge? _____

_____

_____

_____

_____

What did I savor today? _____

_____

_____

_____

_____

What did I do today? _____

_____

_____

_____

_____

What did I feel today? _____

_____

_____

_____

_____

What am I grateful for today? _____

_____

_____

_____

_____

What challenged me today? _____

_____

_____

_____

_____

How can I overcome that challenge? _____

_____

_____

_____

_____

What did I savor today? _____

_____

_____

_____

_____

YEAR ONE

YEAR TWO

BUILDING _the_ BEST YOU THERE IS

_____ _Date_

What did I do today? _____

_____

_____

_____

What did I feel today? _____

_____

_____

_____

What am I grateful for today? _____

_____

_____

_____

What challenged me today? _____

_____

_____

_____

How can I overcome that challenge? _____

_____

_____

_____

What did I savor today? _____

_____

_____

_____

_____ _Date_

What did I do today? _____

_____

_____

_____

What did I feel today? _____

_____

_____

_____

What am I grateful for today? _____

_____

_____

_____

What challenged me today? _____

_____

_____

_____

How can I overcome that challenge? _____

_____

_____

_____

What did I savor today? _____

_____

_____

_____

BUILDING _the_ BEST YOU THERE IS

What did I do today? _____

_____

_____

_____

What did I feel today? _____

_____

_____

_____

What am I grateful for today? _____

_____

_____

_____

What challenged me today? _____

_____

_____

_____

How can I overcome that challenge? _____

_____

_____

_____

What did I savor today? _____

_____

_____

_____

What did I do today? _____

_____

_____

_____

What did I feel today? _____

_____

_____

_____

What am I grateful for today? _____

_____

_____

_____

What challenged me today? _____

_____

_____

_____

How can I overcome that challenge? _____

_____

_____

_____

What did I savor today? _____

_____

_____

_____

_____ Date

What did I do today? _____

_____

_____

_____

What did I feel today? _____

_____

_____

_____

What am I grateful for today? _____

_____

_____

_____

What challenged me today? _____

_____

_____

_____

How can I overcome that challenge? _____

_____

_____

_____

What did I savor today? _____

_____

_____

_____

_____ Date

What did I do today? _____

_____

_____

_____

What did I feel today? _____

_____

_____

_____

What am I grateful for today? _____

_____

_____

_____

What challenged me today? _____

_____

_____

_____

How can I overcome that challenge? _____

_____

_____

_____

What did I savor today? _____

_____

_____

_____

BUILDING _the_ BEST YOU THERE IS

_____ Date

What did I do today? _____

_____
_____
_____
_____

What did I feel today? _____

_____
_____
_____
_____

What am I grateful for today? _____

_____
_____
_____
_____

What challenged me today? _____

_____
_____
_____
_____

How can I overcome that challenge? _____

_____
_____
_____
_____

What did I savor today? _____

_____
_____
_____
_____

YEAR ONE

_____ Date

What did I do today? _____

_____
_____
_____
_____

What did I feel today? _____

_____
_____
_____
_____

What am I grateful for today? _____

_____
_____
_____
_____

What challenged me today? _____

_____
_____
_____
_____

How can I overcome that challenge? _____

_____
_____
_____
_____

What did I savor today? _____

_____
_____
_____
_____

YEAR TWO

_____ Date

What did I do today? _____
_____
_____
_____

What did I feel today? _____
_____
_____
_____

What am I grateful for today? _____
_____
_____
_____

What challenged me today? _____
_____
_____
_____

How can I overcome that challenge? _____
_____
_____
_____

What did I savor today? _____
_____
_____
_____

_____ Date

What did I do today? _____
_____
_____
_____

What did I feel today? _____
_____
_____
_____

What am I grateful for today? _____
_____
_____
_____

What challenged me today? _____
_____
_____
_____

How can I overcome that challenge? _____
_____
_____
_____

What did I savor today? _____
_____
_____
_____

BUILDING _the_ BEST YOU THERE IS

_____ Date

What did I do today? _____
_____
_____
_____
_____

What did I feel today? _____
_____
_____
_____
_____

What am I grateful for today? _____
_____
_____
_____
_____

What challenged me today? _____
_____
_____
_____
_____

How can I overcome that challenge? _____
_____
_____
_____
_____

What did I savor today? _____
_____
_____
_____
_____

YEAR ONE

_____ Date

What did I do today? _____
_____
_____
_____
_____

What did I feel today? _____
_____
_____
_____
_____

What am I grateful for today? _____
_____
_____
_____
_____

What challenged me today? _____
_____
_____
_____
_____

How can I overcome that challenge? _____
_____
_____
_____
_____

What did I savor today? _____
_____
_____
_____
_____

YEAR TWO

BUILDING _the_ BEST YOU THERE IS

_____ Date

What did I do today? _____

_____

_____

_____

What did I feel today? _____

_____

_____

_____

What am I grateful for today? _____

_____

_____

_____

What challenged me today? _____

_____

_____

_____

How can I overcome that challenge? __

_____

_____

_____

What did I savor today? _____

_____

_____

_____

_____ Date

What did I do today? _____

_____

_____

_____

What did I feel today? _____

_____

_____

_____

What am I grateful for today? _____

_____

_____

_____

What challenged me today? _____

_____

_____

_____

How can I overcome that challenge? __

_____

_____

_____

What did I savor today? _____

_____

_____

_____

YEAR ONE

YEAR TWO

BUILDING _the_ BEST YOU THERE IS

_____ Date

What did I do today? _____

_____

_____

_____

What did I feel today? _____

_____

_____

_____

What am I grateful for today? _____

_____

_____

_____

What challenged me today? _____

_____

_____

_____

How can I overcome that challenge? _____

_____

_____

_____

What did I savor today? _____

_____

_____

_____

_____ Date

What did I do today? _____

_____

_____

_____

What did I feel today? _____

_____

_____

_____

What am I grateful for today? _____

_____

_____

_____

What challenged me today? _____

_____

_____

_____

How can I overcome that challenge? _____

_____

_____

_____

What did I savor today? _____

_____

_____

_____

YEAR ONE

YEAR TWO

BUILDING the BEST YOU THERE IS

What did I do today? _____

_____

_____

_____

What did I feel today? _____

_____

_____

_____

What am I grateful for today? _____

_____

_____

_____

What challenged me today? _____

_____

_____

_____

How can I overcome that challenge? _____

_____

_____

_____

What did I savor today? _____

_____

_____

_____

YEAR ONE

What did I do today? _____

_____

_____

_____

What did I feel today? _____

_____

_____

_____

What am I grateful for today? _____

_____

_____

_____

What challenged me today? _____

_____

_____

_____

How can I overcome that challenge? _____

_____

_____

_____

What did I savor today? _____

_____

_____

_____

YEAR TWO

What did I do today? _____
_____
_____
_____
_____

What did I feel today? _____
_____
_____
_____
_____

What am I grateful for today? _____
_____
_____
_____
_____

What challenged me today? _____
_____
_____
_____
_____

How can I overcome that challenge? _____
_____
_____
_____
_____

What did I savor today? _____
_____
_____
_____
_____

What did I do today? _____
_____
_____
_____
_____

What did I feel today? _____
_____
_____
_____
_____

What am I grateful for today? _____
_____
_____
_____
_____

What challenged me today? _____
_____
_____
_____
_____

How can I overcome that challenge? _____
_____
_____
_____
_____

What did I savor today? _____
_____
_____
_____
_____

YEAR ONE

YEAR TWO

BUILDING *the* BEST YOU THERE IS

Date		Date

What did I do today?

_____
_____
_____

What did I feel today?

_____
_____
_____

What am I grateful for today?

_____
_____
_____

What challenged me today?

_____
_____
_____

How can I overcome that challenge?

_____
_____
_____

What did I savor today?

_____
_____
_____

What did I do today?

_____
_____
_____

What did I feel today?

_____
_____
_____

What am I grateful for today?

_____
_____
_____

What challenged me today?

_____
_____
_____

How can I overcome that challenge?

_____
_____
_____

What did I savor today?

_____
_____
_____

YEAR ONE

YEAR TWO

BUILDING *the* BEST YOU THERE IS

What did I do today? _____   What did I do today? _____

_____   _____
_____   _____
_____   _____

What did I feel today? _____   What did I feel today? _____

_____   _____
_____   _____
_____   _____

What am I grateful for today? _____   What am I grateful for today? _____

_____   _____
_____   _____
_____   _____

What challenged me today? _____   What challenged me today? _____

_____   _____
_____   _____
_____   _____

How can I overcome that challenge? _____ How can I overcome that challenge? _____

_____   _____
_____   _____
_____   _____

What did I savor today? _____   What did I savor today? _____

_____   _____
_____   _____
_____   _____

YEAR ONE   YEAR TWO

BUILDING _the_ BEST YOU THERE IS

_____ Date   _____ Date

What did I do today? _____   What did I do today? _____
_____   _____
_____   _____
_____   _____

What did I feel today? _____   What did I feel today? _____
_____   _____
_____   _____
_____   _____

What am I grateful for today? _____   What am I grateful for today? _____
_____   _____
_____   _____
_____   _____

What challenged me today? _____   What challenged me today? _____
_____   _____
_____   _____
_____   _____

How can I overcome that challenge? _____   How can I overcome that challenge? _____
_____   _____
_____   _____
_____   _____

What did I savor today? _____   What did I savor today? _____
_____   _____
_____   _____
_____   _____

YEAR ONE   YEAR TWO

BUILDING _the_ BEST YOU THERE IS

What do I think of myself?

_____

_____

_____

_____

What do other people think of me?

_____

_____

_____

_____

Do I present my true self to others?

_____

_____

_____

_____

Do I show others that I care?

_____

_____

_____

_____

Do I listen to others?

_____

_____

_____

_____

How can I be more tuned in?

_____

_____

_____

_____

BUILDING *the* BEST YOU THERE IS

Do I enjoy getting up in the morning? _____

_____
_____
_____

Do I relish what I do? _____

_____
_____
_____

Do I look forward to life? _____

_____
_____
_____

What would resonate more with me? _____

_____
_____
_____

Do I see the road to fulfillment? _____

_____
_____
_____

How do I take that path? _____

_____
_____
_____

What do I think of myself? _____

_____

_____

_____

_____

What do other people think of me? _____

_____

_____

_____

_____

Do I present my true self to others? _____

_____

_____

_____

_____

_____

Do I show others that I care? _____

_____

_____

_____

_____

Do I listen to others? _____

_____

_____

_____

_____

How can I be more tuned in? _____

_____

_____

_____

_____

BUILDING *the* BEST YOU THERE IS

Do I enjoy getting up in the morning?

Do I relish what I do?

Do I look forward to life?

What would resonate more with me?

Do I see the road to fulfillment?

How do I take that path?

What did I do today? _____

What did I do today? _____

_____

_____

_____

_____

_____

_____

What did I feel today? _____

What did I feel today? _____

_____

_____

_____

_____

_____

_____

What am I grateful for today? _____

What am I grateful for today? _____

_____

_____

_____

_____

_____

_____

What challenged me today? _____

What challenged me today? _____

_____

_____

_____

_____

_____

_____

How can I overcome that challenge? ___

How can I overcome that challenge? ___

_____

_____

_____

_____

_____

_____

What did I savor today? _____

What did I savor today? _____

_____

_____

_____

_____

_____

_____

	Date _____		Date _____

What did I do today? _____

_____
_____
_____

What did I feel today? _____

_____
_____
_____

What am I grateful for today? _____

_____
_____
_____

What challenged me today? _____

_____
_____
_____

How can I overcome that challenge? _____

_____
_____
_____

What did I savor today? _____

_____
_____
_____

What did I do today? _____

_____
_____
_____

What did I feel today? _____

_____
_____
_____

What am I grateful for today? _____

_____
_____
_____

What challenged me today? _____

_____
_____
_____

How can I overcome that challenge? _____

_____
_____
_____

What did I savor today? _____

_____
_____
_____

YEAR ONE

YEAR TWO

BUILDING _the_ BEST YOU THERE IS

_____ Date

What did I do today? _____

_____
_____
_____
_____

What did I feel today? _____

_____
_____
_____
_____

What am I grateful for today? _____

_____
_____
_____
_____

What challenged me today? _____

_____
_____
_____
_____

How can I overcome that challenge? _____

_____
_____
_____
_____

What did I savor today? _____

_____
_____
_____
_____

YEAR ONE

_____ Date

What did I do today? _____

_____
_____
_____
_____

What did I feel today? _____

_____
_____
_____
_____

What am I grateful for today? _____

_____
_____
_____
_____

What challenged me today? _____

_____
_____
_____
_____

How can I overcome that challenge? _____

_____
_____
_____
_____

What did I savor today? _____

_____
_____
_____
_____

YEAR TWO

BUILDING *the* BEST YOU THERE IS

_____ Date

What did I do today? _____

_____

_____

_____

_____

What did I feel today? _____

_____

_____

_____

What am I grateful for today? _____

_____

_____

_____

What challenged me today? _____

_____

_____

_____

How can I overcome that challenge? _____

_____

_____

_____

What did I savor today? _____

_____

_____

_____

_____ Date

What did I do today? _____

_____

_____

_____

_____

What did I feel today? _____

_____

_____

_____

What am I grateful for today? _____

_____

_____

_____

What challenged me today? _____

_____

_____

_____

How can I overcome that challenge? _____

_____

_____

_____

What did I savor today? _____

_____

_____

_____

BUILDING *the* BEST YOU THERE IS

_____ Date

What did I do today? _____

_____

_____

_____

_____

What did I feel today? _____

_____

_____

_____

_____

What am I grateful for today? _____

_____

_____

_____

_____

What challenged me today? _____

_____

_____

_____

_____

How can I overcome that challenge? _____

_____

_____

_____

_____

What did I savor today? _____

_____

_____

_____

YEAR ONE

_____ Date

What did I do today? _____

_____

_____

_____

_____

What did I feel today? _____

_____

_____

_____

_____

What am I grateful for today? _____

_____

_____

_____

_____

What challenged me today? _____

_____

_____

_____

_____

How can I overcome that challenge? _____

_____

_____

_____

_____

What did I savor today? _____

_____

_____

_____

YEAR TWO

BUILDING _the_ BEST YOU THERE IS

_____ Date

What did I do today? _____

_____

_____

_____

_____

What did I feel today? _____

_____

_____

_____

What am I grateful for today? _____

_____

_____

_____

What challenged me today? _____

_____

_____

_____

How can I overcome that challenge? ____

_____

_____

_____

What did I savor today? _____

_____

_____

_____

_____

YEAR ONE

_____ Date

What did I do today? _____

_____

_____

_____

_____

What did I feel today? _____

_____

_____

_____

What am I grateful for today? _____

_____

_____

_____

What challenged me today? _____

_____

_____

_____

How can I overcome that challenge? ____

_____

_____

_____

What did I savor today? _____

_____

_____

_____

_____

YEAR TWO

BUILDING _the_ BEST YOU THERE IS

_____ Date   _____ Date

What did I do today? _____   What did I do today? _____
_____   _____
_____   _____
_____   _____
_____   _____

What did I feel today? _____   What did I feel today? _____
_____   _____
_____   _____
_____   _____
_____   _____

What am I grateful for today? _____   What am I grateful for today? _____
_____   _____
_____   _____
_____   _____
_____   _____

What challenged me today? _____   What challenged me today? _____
_____   _____
_____   _____
_____   _____
_____   _____

How can I overcome that challenge? ____   How can I overcome that challenge? ____
_____   _____
_____   _____
_____   _____
_____   _____

What did I savor today? _____   What did I savor today? _____
_____   _____
_____   _____
_____   _____
_____   _____

YEAR ONE   YEAR TWO

BUILDING _the_ BEST YOU THERE IS

_____ Date

What did I do today? _____
_____
_____
_____
_____

What did I feel today? _____
_____
_____
_____
_____

What am I grateful for today? _____
_____
_____
_____
_____

What challenged me today? _____
_____
_____
_____
_____

How can I overcome that challenge? ___
_____
_____
_____
_____

What did I savor today? _____
_____
_____
_____

YEAR ONE

_____ Date

What did I do today? _____
_____
_____
_____
_____

What did I feel today? _____
_____
_____
_____
_____

What am I grateful for today? _____
_____
_____
_____
_____

What challenged me today? _____
_____
_____
_____
_____

How can I overcome that challenge? ___
_____
_____
_____
_____

What did I savor today? _____
_____
_____
_____

YEAR TWO

BUILDING _the_ BEST YOU THERE IS

_____ Date

What did I do today? _____
_____
_____
_____
_____

What did I feel today? _____
_____
_____
_____
_____

What am I grateful for today? _____
_____
_____
_____
_____

What challenged me today? _____
_____
_____
_____
_____

How can I overcome that challenge? ___
_____
_____
_____
_____

What did I savor today? _____
_____
_____
_____
_____

YEAR ONE

_____ Date

What did I do today? _____
_____
_____
_____
_____

What did I feel today? _____
_____
_____
_____
_____

What am I grateful for today? _____
_____
_____
_____
_____

What challenged me today? _____
_____
_____
_____
_____

How can I overcome that challenge? ___
_____
_____
_____
_____

What did I savor today? _____
_____
_____
_____
_____

YEAR TWO

What did I do today? _____

_____

_____

_____

What did I feel today? _____

_____

_____

_____

What am I grateful for today? _____

_____

_____

_____

What challenged me today? _____

_____

_____

_____

How can I overcome that challenge? _____

_____

_____

_____

What did I savor today? _____

_____

_____

_____

_____

What did I do today? _____

_____

_____

_____

What did I feel today? _____

_____

_____

_____

What am I grateful for today? _____

_____

_____

_____

What challenged me today? _____

_____

_____

_____

How can I overcome that challenge? _____

_____

_____

_____

What did I savor today? _____

_____

_____

_____

_____

YEAR ONE

YEAR TWO

BUILDING *the* BEST YOU THERE IS

_____ Date

What did I do today? _____
_____
_____
_____
_____

What did I feel today? _____
_____
_____
_____
_____

What am I grateful for today? _____
_____
_____
_____

What challenged me today? _____
_____
_____
_____
_____

How can I overcome that challenge? _____
_____
_____
_____
_____

What did I savor today? _____
_____
_____
_____
_____

YEAR ONE

_____ Date

What did I do today? _____
_____
_____
_____
_____

What did I feel today? _____
_____
_____
_____
_____

What am I grateful for today? _____
_____
_____
_____

What challenged me today? _____
_____
_____
_____
_____

How can I overcome that challenge? _____
_____
_____
_____
_____

What did I savor today? _____
_____
_____
_____
_____

YEAR TWO

BUILDING _the_ BEST YOU THERE IS

What did I do today? _____

_____

_____

_____

_____

What did I feel today? _____

_____

_____

_____

_____

What am I grateful for today? _____

_____

_____

_____

_____

What challenged me today? _____

_____

_____

_____

_____

How can I overcome that challenge? _____

_____

_____

_____

_____

What did I savor today? _____

_____

_____

_____

_____

What did I do today? _____

_____

_____

_____

_____

What did I feel today? _____

_____

_____

_____

_____

What am I grateful for today? _____

_____

_____

_____

_____

What challenged me today? _____

_____

_____

_____

_____

How can I overcome that challenge? _____

_____

_____

_____

_____

What did I savor today? _____

_____

_____

_____

_____

YEAR ONE

YEAR TWO

BUILDING *the* BEST YOU THERE IS

What did I do today? _____

What did I feel today? _____

What am I grateful for today? _____

What challenged me today? _____

How can I overcome that challenge? _____

What did I savor today? _____

What did I do today? _____

What did I feel today? _____

What am I grateful for today? _____

What challenged me today? _____

How can I overcome that challenge? _____

What did I savor today? _____

_____ Date

What did I do today? _____
_____
_____
_____
_____

What did I feel today? _____
_____
_____
_____
_____

What am I grateful for today? _____
_____
_____
_____
_____

What challenged me today? _____
_____
_____
_____
_____

How can I overcome that challenge? _____
_____
_____
_____
_____

What did I savor today? _____
_____
_____
_____
_____

YEAR ONE

_____ Date

What did I do today? _____
_____
_____
_____
_____

What did I feel today? _____
_____
_____
_____
_____

What am I grateful for today? _____
_____
_____
_____
_____

What challenged me today? _____
_____
_____
_____
_____

How can I overcome that challenge? _____
_____
_____
_____
_____

What did I savor today? _____
_____
_____
_____
_____

YEAR TWO

BUILDING *the* BEST YOU THERE IS

What did I do today? _____

What did I feel today? _____

What am I grateful for today? _____

What challenged me today? _____

How can I overcome that challenge? _____

What did I savor today? _____

What did I do today? _____

What did I feel today? _____

What am I grateful for today? _____

What challenged me today? _____

How can I overcome that challenge? _____

What did I savor today? _____

_____ Date

What did I do today? _____

_____
_____
_____
_____

What did I feel today? _____

_____
_____
_____
_____

What am I grateful for today? _____

_____
_____
_____
_____

What challenged me today? _____

_____
_____
_____
_____

How can I overcome that challenge? _____

_____
_____
_____
_____

What did I savor today? _____

_____
_____
_____
_____

_____ Date

What did I do today? _____

_____
_____
_____
_____

What did I feel today? _____

_____
_____
_____
_____

What am I grateful for today? _____

_____
_____
_____
_____

What challenged me today? _____

_____
_____
_____
_____

How can I overcome that challenge? _____

_____
_____
_____
_____

What did I savor today? _____

_____
_____
_____
_____

YEAR ONE

YEAR TWO

BUILDING *the* BEST YOU THERE IS

_____ Date

What did I do today? _____
_____
_____
_____
_____

What did I feel today? _____
_____
_____
_____
_____

What am I grateful for today? _____
_____
_____
_____
_____

What challenged me today? _____
_____
_____
_____
_____

How can I overcome that challenge? _____
_____
_____
_____
_____

What did I savor today? _____
_____
_____
_____
_____

YEAR ONE

_____ Date

What did I do today? _____
_____
_____
_____
_____

What did I feel today? _____
_____
_____
_____
_____

What am I grateful for today? _____
_____
_____
_____
_____

What challenged me today? _____
_____
_____
_____
_____

How can I overcome that challenge? _____
_____
_____
_____
_____

What did I savor today? _____
_____
_____
_____
_____

YEAR TWO

BUILDING _the_ BEST YOU THERE IS

_____ Date

What did I do today? _____
_____
_____
_____
_____

What did I feel today? _____
_____
_____
_____
_____

What am I grateful for today? _____
_____
_____
_____
_____

What challenged me today? _____
_____
_____
_____
_____

How can I overcome that challenge? _____
_____
_____
_____
_____

What did I savor today? _____
_____
_____
_____
_____

_____ Date

What did I do today? _____
_____
_____
_____
_____

What did I feel today? _____
_____
_____
_____
_____

What am I grateful for today? _____
_____
_____
_____
_____

What challenged me today? _____
_____
_____
_____
_____

How can I overcome that challenge? _____
_____
_____
_____
_____

What did I savor today? _____
_____
_____
_____
_____

What did I do today? _____   What did I do today? _____
_____   _____
_____   _____
_____   _____
_____   _____

What did I feel today? _____   What did I feel today? _____
_____   _____
_____   _____
_____   _____
_____   _____

What am I grateful for today? _____   What am I grateful for today? _____
_____   _____
_____   _____
_____   _____
_____   _____

What challenged me today? _____   What challenged me today? _____
_____   _____
_____   _____
_____   _____
_____   _____

How can I overcome that challenge? _____   How can I overcome that challenge? _____
_____   _____
_____   _____
_____   _____
_____   _____

What did I savor today? _____   What did I savor today? _____
_____   _____
_____   _____
_____   _____
_____   _____

YEAR ONE   YEAR TWO

BUILDING the BEST YOU THERE IS

_____ Date   _____ Date

What did I do today? _____   *What did I do today?* _____

_____   _____

_____   _____

_____   _____

_____   _____

What did I feel today? _____   *What did I feel today?* _____

_____   _____

_____   _____

_____   _____

_____   _____

What am I grateful for today? _____   *What am I grateful for today?* _____

_____   _____

_____   _____

_____   _____

_____   _____

What challenged me today? _____   *What challenged me today?* _____

_____   _____

_____   _____

_____   _____

_____   _____

How can I overcome that challenge? _____   *How can I overcome that challenge?* _____

_____   _____

_____   _____

_____   _____

_____   _____

What did I savor today? _____   *What did I savor today?* _____

_____   _____

_____   _____

_____   _____

_____   _____

_____ Date   _____ Date

What did I do today? _____   What did I do today? _____
_____   _____
_____   _____
_____   _____
_____   _____

What did I feel today? _____   What did I feel today? _____
_____   _____
_____   _____
_____   _____
_____   _____

What am I grateful for today? _____ What am I grateful for today? _____
_____   _____
_____   _____
_____   _____
_____   _____

What challenged me today? _____   What challenged me today? _____
_____   _____
_____   _____
_____   _____
_____   _____

How can I overcome that challenge? ___ How can I overcome that challenge? ___
_____   _____
_____   _____
_____   _____
_____   _____

What did I savor today? _____   What did I savor today? _____
_____   _____
_____   _____
_____   _____

YEAR ONE   YEAR TWO

BUILDING the BEST YOU THERE IS

| Date | Date |

What did I do today? _____

_____

_____

_____

What did I feel today? _____

_____

_____

_____

What am I grateful for today? _____

_____

_____

_____

What challenged me today? _____

_____

_____

_____

How can I overcome that challenge? _____

_____

_____

_____

What did I savor today? _____

_____

_____

_____

What did I do today? _____

_____

_____

_____

What did I feel today? _____

_____

_____

_____

What am I grateful for today? _____

_____

_____

_____

What challenged me today? _____

_____

_____

_____

How can I overcome that challenge? _____

_____

_____

_____

What did I savor today? _____

_____

_____

_____

YEAR ONE   YEAR TWO

BUILDING *the* BEST YOU THERE IS

What did I do today? ————   *What did I do today?* ————

————————   ————————
————————   ————————
————————   ————————
————————   ————————

What did I feel today? ————   *What did I feel today?* ————

————————   ————————
————————   ————————
————————   ————————
————————   ————————

What am I grateful for today? ————   *What am I grateful for today?* ————

————————   ————————
————————   ————————
————————   ————————
————————   ————————

What challenged me today? ————   *What challenged me today?* ————

————————   ————————
————————   ————————
————————   ————————
————————   ————————

How can I overcome that challenge? ————   *How can I overcome that challenge?* ————

————————   ————————
————————   ————————
————————   ————————
————————   ————————

What did I savor today? ————   *What did I savor today?* ————

————————   ————————
————————   ————————
————————   ————————
————————   ————————

YEAR ONE   YEAR TWO

BUILDING *the* BEST YOU THERE IS

_____ Date

What did I do today? _____
_____
_____
_____
_____

What did I feel today? _____
_____
_____
_____

What am I grateful for today? _____
_____
_____
_____

What challenged me today? _____
_____
_____
_____

How can I overcome that challenge? _____
_____
_____
_____

What did I savor today? _____
_____
_____
_____

YEAR ONE

_____ Date

What did I do today? _____
_____
_____
_____
_____

What did I feel today? _____
_____
_____
_____

What am I grateful for today? _____
_____
_____
_____

What challenged me today? _____
_____
_____
_____

How can I overcome that challenge? _____
_____
_____
_____

What did I savor today? _____
_____
_____
_____

YEAR TWO

BUILDING *the* BEST YOU THERE IS

What did I do today? _____

_____
_____
_____
_____

What did I feel today? _____

_____
_____
_____
_____

What am I grateful for today? _____

_____
_____
_____
_____

What challenged me today? _____

_____
_____
_____
_____

How can I overcome that challenge? _____

_____
_____
_____
_____

What did I savor today? _____

_____
_____
_____
_____

What did I do today? _____

_____
_____
_____
_____

What did I feel today? _____

_____
_____
_____
_____

What am I grateful for today? _____

_____
_____
_____
_____

What challenged me today? _____

_____
_____
_____
_____

How can I overcome that challenge? _____

_____
_____
_____
_____

What did I savor today? _____

_____
_____
_____
_____

_____ Date

What did I do today? _____
_____
_____
_____
_____

What did I feel today? _____
_____
_____
_____
_____

What am I grateful for today? _____
_____
_____
_____
_____

What challenged me today? _____
_____
_____
_____
_____

How can I overcome that challenge? _____
_____
_____
_____
_____

What did I savor today? _____
_____
_____
_____
_____

YEAR ONE

_____ Date

What did I do today? _____
_____
_____
_____
_____

What did I feel today? _____
_____
_____
_____
_____

What am I grateful for today? _____
_____
_____
_____
_____

What challenged me today? _____
_____
_____
_____
_____

How can I overcome that challenge? _____
_____
_____
_____
_____

What did I savor today? _____
_____
_____
_____
_____

YEAR TWO

BUILDING the BEST YOU THERE IS

_____ Date

What did I do today? _____

_____

_____

_____

_____

What did I feel today? _____

_____

_____

_____

_____

What am I grateful for today? _____

_____

_____

_____

_____

What challenged me today? _____

_____

_____

_____

_____

How can I overcome that challenge? _____

_____

_____

_____

_____

What did I savor today? _____

_____

_____

_____

_____

YEAR ONE

_____ Date

What did I do today? _____

_____

_____

_____

_____

What did I feel today? _____

_____

_____

_____

_____

What am I grateful for today? _____

_____

_____

_____

_____

What challenged me today? _____

_____

_____

_____

_____

How can I overcome that challenge? _____

_____

_____

_____

_____

What did I savor today? _____

_____

_____

_____

_____

YEAR TWO

BUILDING _the_ BEST YOU THERE IS

_____ Date

What did I do today? _____
_____
_____
_____

What did I feel today? _____
_____
_____
_____

What am I grateful for today? _____
_____
_____
_____

What challenged me today? _____
_____
_____
_____

How can I overcome that challenge? ____
_____
_____
_____

What did I savor today? _____
_____
_____
_____

Year One

_____ Date

What did I do today? _____
_____
_____
_____

What did I feel today? _____
_____
_____
_____

What am I grateful for today? _____
_____
_____
_____

What challenged me today? _____
_____
_____
_____

How can I overcome that challenge? ____
_____
_____
_____

What did I savor today? _____
_____
_____
_____

Year Two

BUILDING *the* BEST YOU THERE IS

_____ Date

What did I do today? _____

_____

_____

_____

What did I feel today? _____

_____

_____

_____

What am I grateful for today? _____

_____

_____

_____

What challenged me today? _____

_____

_____

_____

How can I overcome that challenge? ____

_____

_____

_____

What did I savor today? _____

_____

_____

_____

YEAR ONE

_____ Date

What did I do today? _____

_____

_____

_____

What did I feel today? _____

_____

_____

_____

What am I grateful for today? _____

_____

_____

_____

What challenged me today? _____

_____

_____

_____

How can I overcome that challenge? ____

_____

_____

_____

What did I savor today? _____

_____

_____

_____

YEAR TWO

BUILDING *the* BEST YOU THERE IS

_____ Date

What did I do today? _____
_____
_____
_____
_____

What did I feel today? _____
_____
_____
_____
_____

What am I grateful for today? _____
_____
_____
_____
_____

What challenged me today? _____
_____
_____
_____
_____

How can I overcome that challenge? _____
_____
_____
_____
_____

What did I savor today? _____
_____
_____
_____
_____

YEAR ONE

_____ Date

What did I do today? _____
_____
_____
_____
_____

What did I feel today? _____
_____
_____
_____
_____

What am I grateful for today? _____
_____
_____
_____
_____

What challenged me today? _____
_____
_____
_____
_____

How can I overcome that challenge? _____
_____
_____
_____
_____

What did I savor today? _____
_____
_____
_____
_____

YEAR TWO

BUILDING *the* BEST YOU THERE IS

_____ Date

What did I do today? _____
_____
_____
_____
_____

What did I feel today? _____
_____
_____
_____
_____

What am I grateful for today? _____
_____
_____
_____
_____

What challenged me today? _____
_____
_____
_____
_____

How can I overcome that challenge? ___
_____
_____
_____
_____

What did I savor today? _____
_____
_____
_____
_____

YEAR ONE

_____ Date

What did I do today? _____
_____
_____
_____
_____

What did I feel today? _____
_____
_____
_____
_____

What am I grateful for today? _____
_____
_____
_____
_____

What challenged me today? _____
_____
_____
_____
_____

How can I overcome that challenge? ___
_____
_____
_____
_____

What did I savor today? _____
_____
_____
_____
_____

YEAR TWO

BUILDING the BEST YOU THERE IS

_____ Date   _____ Date

What did I do today? _____   What did I do today? _____

_____   _____

_____   _____

_____   _____

_____   _____

What did I feel today? _____   What did I feel today? _____

_____   _____

_____   _____

_____   _____

_____   _____

What am I grateful for today? _____   What am I grateful for today? _____

_____   _____

_____   _____

_____   _____

_____   _____

What challenged me today? _____   What challenged me today? _____

_____   _____

_____   _____

_____   _____

_____   _____

How can I overcome that challenge? ___   How can I overcome that challenge? ___

_____   _____

_____   _____

_____   _____

_____   _____

What did I savor today? _____   What did I savor today? _____

_____   _____

_____   _____

_____   _____

YEAR ONE   YEAR TWO

BUILDING *the* BEST YOU THERE IS

_____ Date

What did I do today? _____
_____
_____
_____
_____

What did I feel today? _____
_____
_____
_____
_____

What am I grateful for today? _____
_____
_____
_____
_____

What challenged me today? _____
_____
_____
_____
_____

How can I overcome that challenge? _____
_____
_____
_____
_____

What did I savor today? _____
_____
_____
_____
_____

Year One

_____ Date

What did I do today? _____
_____
_____
_____
_____

What did I feel today? _____
_____
_____
_____
_____

What am I grateful for today? _____
_____
_____
_____
_____

What challenged me today? _____
_____
_____
_____
_____

How can I overcome that challenge? _____
_____
_____
_____
_____

What did I savor today? _____
_____
_____
_____
_____

Year Two

BUILDING _the_ BEST YOU THERE IS

_____ Date   _____ Date

What did I do today? _____   What did I do today? _____
_____   _____
_____   _____
_____   _____
_____   _____

What did I feel today? _____   What did I feel today? _____
_____   _____
_____   _____
_____   _____
_____   _____

What am I grateful for today? _____   What am I grateful for today? _____
_____   _____
_____   _____
_____   _____
_____   _____

What challenged me today? _____   What challenged me today? _____
_____   _____
_____   _____
_____   _____
_____   _____

How can I overcome that challenge? ____   How can I overcome that challenge? ____
_____   _____
_____   _____
_____   _____
_____   _____

What did I savor today? _____   What did I savor today? _____
_____   _____
_____   _____
_____   _____

YEAR ONE   YEAR TWO

BUILDING _the_ BEST YOU THERE IS

What did I do today? _____

What did I do today? _____

_____

_____

_____

_____

_____

_____

_____

_____

What did I feel today? _____

What did I feel today? _____

_____

_____

_____

_____

_____

_____

_____

_____

What am I grateful for today? _____

What am I grateful for today? _____

_____

_____

_____

_____

_____

_____

_____

_____

What challenged me today? _____

What challenged me today? _____

_____

_____

_____

_____

_____

_____

_____

_____

How can I overcome that challenge? _____

How can I overcome that challenge? _____

_____

_____

_____

_____

_____

_____

_____

_____

What did I savor today? _____

What did I savor today? _____

_____

_____

_____

_____

_____

_____

_____

_____

YEAR ONE

YEAR TWO

BUILDING the BEST YOU THERE IS

_____ Date   _____ Date

What did I do today? _____   *What did I do today?* _____

_____

_____

_____

_____

What did I feel today? _____   *What did I feel today?* _____

_____

_____

_____

What am I grateful for today? _____   *What am I grateful for today?* _____

_____

_____

_____

_____

What challenged me today? _____   *What challenged me today?* _____

_____

_____

_____

How can I overcome that challenge? _____   *How can I overcome that challenge?* _____

_____

_____

_____

_____

What did I savor today? _____   *What did I savor today?* _____

_____

_____

_____

_____

BUILDING *the* BEST YOU THERE IS

What did I do today? _____

_____

_____

_____

_____

What did I feel today? _____

_____

_____

_____

_____

What am I grateful for today? _____

_____

_____

_____

_____

What challenged me today? _____

_____

_____

_____

_____

How can I overcome that challenge? _____

_____

_____

_____

_____

What did I savor today? _____

_____

_____

_____

What did I do today? _____

_____

_____

_____

_____

What did I feel today? _____

_____

_____

_____

_____

What am I grateful for today? _____

_____

_____

_____

_____

What challenged me today? _____

_____

_____

_____

_____

How can I overcome that challenge? _____

_____

_____

_____

_____

What did I savor today? _____

_____

_____

_____

YEAR ONE   YEAR TWO

BUILDING *the* BEST YOU THERE IS

_____ Date   _____ Date

What did I do today? _____   *What did I do today?* _____
_____   _____
_____   _____
_____   _____
_____   _____

What did I feel today? _____   *What did I feel today?* _____
_____   _____
_____   _____
_____   _____
_____   _____

What am I grateful for today? _____ *What am I grateful for today?* _____
_____   _____
_____   _____
_____   _____
_____   _____

What challenged me today? _____   *What challenged me today?* _____
_____   _____
_____   _____
_____   _____
_____   _____

How can I overcome that challenge? ___ *How can I overcome that challenge?* ___
_____   _____
_____   _____
_____   _____
_____   _____

What did I savor today? _____   *What did I savor today?* _____
_____   _____
_____   _____
_____   _____
_____   _____

Year One   Year Two

BUILDING *the* BEST YOU THERE IS

_____ Date

What did I do today? _____

_____

_____

_____

_____

What did I feel today? _____

_____

_____

_____

_____

What am I grateful for today? _____

_____

_____

_____

_____

What challenged me today? _____

_____

_____

_____

_____

How can I overcome that challenge? _____

_____

_____

_____

_____

What did I savor today? _____

_____

_____

_____

_____

YEAR ONE

What did I do today? _____

_____

_____

_____

_____

What did I feel today? _____

_____

_____

_____

_____

What am I grateful for today? _____

_____

_____

_____

_____

What challenged me today? _____

_____

_____

_____

_____

How can I overcome that challenge? _____

_____

_____

_____

_____

What did I savor today? _____

_____

_____

_____

_____

YEAR TWO

_____ Date   _____ Date

What did I do today? _____   *What did I do today?* _____
_____   _____
_____   _____
_____   _____

What did I feel today? _____   *What did I feel today?* _____
_____   _____
_____   _____
_____   _____

What am I grateful for today? _____   *What am I grateful for today?* _____
_____   _____
_____   _____
_____   _____

What challenged me today? _____   *What challenged me today?* _____
_____   _____
_____   _____
_____   _____

How can I overcome that challenge? _____   *How can I overcome that challenge?* _____
_____   _____
_____   _____
_____   _____

What did I savor today? _____   *What did I savor today?* _____
_____   _____
_____   _____
_____   _____

YEAR ONE   YEAR TWO

BUILDING *the* BEST YOU THERE IS

What did I do today? _____

What did I do today? _____

_____

_____

_____

_____

_____

_____

_____

_____

What did I feel today? _____

What did I feel today? _____

_____

_____

_____

_____

_____

_____

_____

_____

What am I grateful for today? _____

What am I grateful for today? _____

_____

_____

_____

_____

_____

_____

_____

_____

What challenged me today? _____

What challenged me today? _____

_____

_____

_____

_____

_____

_____

_____

_____

How can I overcome that challenge? ____

How can I overcome that challenge? ____

_____

_____

_____

_____

_____

_____

_____

_____

What did I savor today? _____

What did I savor today? _____

_____

_____

_____

_____

_____

_____

YEAR ONE

YEAR TWO

BUILDING *the* BEST YOU THERE IS

_____ Date

What did I do today? _____

_____
_____
_____
_____

What did I feel today? _____

_____
_____
_____

What am I grateful for today? _____

_____
_____
_____

What challenged me today? _____

_____
_____
_____

How can I overcome that challenge? _____

_____
_____
_____

What did I savor today? _____

_____
_____
_____

_____ Date

What did I do today? _____

_____
_____
_____
_____

What did I feel today? _____

_____
_____
_____

What am I grateful for today? _____

_____
_____
_____

What challenged me today? _____

_____
_____
_____

How can I overcome that challenge? _____

_____
_____
_____

What did I savor today? _____

_____
_____
_____

BUILDING _the_ BEST YOU THERE IS

_____ Date   _____ Date

What did I do today? _____   What did I do today? _____
_____   _____
_____   _____
_____   _____
_____   _____

What did I feel today? _____   What did I feel today? _____
_____   _____
_____   _____
_____   _____
_____   _____

What am I grateful for today? _____   What am I grateful for today? _____
_____   _____
_____   _____
_____   _____
_____   _____

What challenged me today? _____   What challenged me today? _____
_____   _____
_____   _____
_____   _____
_____   _____

How can I overcome that challenge? ___ How can I overcome that challenge? ___
_____   _____
_____   _____
_____   _____
_____   _____

What did I savor today? _____   What did I savor today? _____
_____   _____
_____   _____
_____   _____
_____   _____

YEAR ONE   YEAR TWO

BUILDING *the* BEST YOU THERE IS

What did I do today? _____

What did I do today? _____

What did I feel today? _____

What did I feel today? _____

What am I grateful for today? _____

What am I grateful for today? _____

What challenged me today? _____

What challenged me today? _____

How can I overcome that challenge? _____

How can I overcome that challenge? _____

What did I savor today? _____

What did I savor today? _____

YEAR ONE

YEAR TWO

BUILDING *the* BEST YOU THERE IS

_____ Date

What did I do today? _____
_____
_____
_____

What did I feel today? _____
_____
_____
_____

What am I grateful for today? _____
_____
_____
_____

What challenged me today? _____
_____
_____
_____

How can I overcome that challenge? _____
_____
_____
_____

What did I savor today? _____
_____
_____
_____

YEAR ONE

_____ Date

What did I do today? _____
_____
_____
_____

What did I feel today? _____
_____
_____
_____

What am I grateful for today? _____
_____
_____
_____

What challenged me today? _____
_____
_____
_____

How can I overcome that challenge? _____
_____
_____
_____

What did I savor today? _____
_____
_____
_____

YEAR TWO

BUILDING *the* BEST YOU THERE IS

_____ Date

What did I do today? _____
_____
_____
_____
_____

What did I feel today? _____
_____
_____
_____
_____

What am I grateful for today? _____
_____
_____
_____
_____

What challenged me today? _____
_____
_____
_____
_____

How can I overcome that challenge? _____
_____
_____
_____
_____

What did I savor today? _____
_____
_____
_____
_____

YEAR ONE

_____ Date

What did I do today? _____
_____
_____
_____
_____

What did I feel today? _____
_____
_____
_____
_____

What am I grateful for today? _____
_____
_____
_____
_____

What challenged me today? _____
_____
_____
_____
_____

How can I overcome that challenge? _____
_____
_____
_____
_____

What did I savor today? _____
_____
_____
_____
_____

YEAR TWO

BUILDING *the* BEST YOU THERE IS

_____ Date

What did I do today? _____

_____

_____

_____

_____

What did I feel today? _____

_____

_____

_____

_____

What am I grateful for today? _____

_____

_____

_____

_____

What challenged me today? _____

_____

_____

_____

_____

How can I overcome that challenge? _____

_____

_____

_____

_____

What did I savor today? _____

_____

_____

_____

_____

YEAR ONE

_____ Date

What did I do today? _____

_____

_____

_____

_____

What did I feel today? _____

_____

_____

_____

_____

What am I grateful for today? _____

_____

_____

_____

_____

What challenged me today? _____

_____

_____

_____

_____

How can I overcome that challenge? _____

_____

_____

_____

_____

What did I savor today? _____

_____

_____

_____

_____

YEAR TWO

BUILDING the BEST YOU THERE IS

_____ Date

What did I do today? _____

_____

_____

_____

What did I feel today? _____

_____

_____

_____

What am I grateful for today? _____

_____

_____

_____

What challenged me today? _____

_____

_____

_____

How can I overcome that challenge? _____

_____

_____

_____

What did I savor today? _____

_____

_____

_____

YEAR ONE

_____ Date

What did I do today? _____

_____

_____

_____

What did I feel today? _____

_____

_____

_____

What am I grateful for today? _____

_____

_____

_____

What challenged me today? _____

_____

_____

_____

How can I overcome that challenge? _____

_____

_____

_____

What did I savor today? _____

_____

_____

_____

YEAR TWO

BUILDING _the_ BEST YOU THERE IS

Do I enjoy spending time with others? _____
_____
_____
_____
_____

Would I like to connect with more people? _____
_____
_____
_____
_____

Do I feel happy when I'm alone? _____
_____
_____
_____
_____

Do I feel safe and secure when I'm by myself? _____
_____
_____
_____
_____

Do I need others to feel whole? _____
_____
_____
_____
_____

Does my life include other people? _____
_____
_____
_____
_____

What was my high point in the preceding weeks? _____
_____
_____
_____
_____

What was the low point? _____
_____
_____
_____
_____

Did the time flow smoothly? _____
_____
_____
_____
_____

Did I create goals? _____
_____
_____
_____
_____

Did I work towards those goals? _____
_____
_____
_____
_____

Did I achieve those goals? _____
_____
_____
_____
_____

BUILDING *the* BEST YOU THERE IS

Do I enjoy spending time with others? _____
_____
_____
_____
_____

Would I like to connect with more people? _____
_____
_____
_____
_____

Do I feel happy when I'm alone? _____
_____
_____
_____
_____

Do I feel safe and secure when I'm by myself? _____
_____
_____
_____
_____

Do I need others to feel whole? _____
_____
_____
_____
_____

Does my life include other people? _____
_____
_____
_____
_____

What was my high point in the preceding weeks? _____

_____

_____

_____

_____

What was the low point? _____

_____

_____

_____

_____

Did the time flow smoothly? _____

_____

_____

_____

_____

Did I create goals? _____

_____

_____

_____

_____

Did I work towards those goals? _____

_____

_____

_____

_____

Did I achieve those goals? _____

_____

_____

_____

_____

_____ Date

What did I do today? _____

_____
_____
_____
_____

What did I feel today? _____

_____
_____
_____
_____

What am I grateful for today? _____

_____
_____
_____
_____

What challenged me today? _____

_____
_____
_____
_____

How can I overcome that challenge? _____

_____
_____
_____
_____

What did I savor today? _____

_____
_____
_____
_____

YEAR ONE

_____ Date

What did I do today? _____

_____
_____
_____
_____

What did I feel today? _____

_____
_____
_____
_____

What am I grateful for today? _____

_____
_____
_____
_____

What challenged me today? _____

_____
_____
_____
_____

How can I overcome that challenge? _____

_____
_____
_____
_____

What did I savor today? _____

_____
_____
_____
_____

YEAR TWO

BUILDING *the* BEST YOU THERE IS

_____ Date   _____ Date

What did I do today? _____   What did I do today? _____
_____   _____
_____   _____
_____   _____

What did I feel today? _____   What did I feel today? _____
_____   _____
_____   _____
_____   _____

What am I grateful for today? _____   What am I grateful for today? _____
_____   _____
_____   _____
_____   _____

What challenged me today? _____   What challenged me today? _____
_____   _____
_____   _____
_____   _____

How can I overcome that challenge? _____   How can I overcome that challenge? _____
_____   _____
_____   _____
_____   _____

What did I savor today? _____   What did I savor today? _____
_____   _____
_____   _____
_____   _____

YEAR ONE   YEAR TWO

BUILDING _the_ BEST YOU THERE IS

What did I do today? _____

_____

_____

_____

_____

What did I feel today? _____

_____

_____

_____

_____

What am I grateful for today? _____

_____

_____

_____

_____

What challenged me today? _____

_____

_____

_____

_____

How can I overcome that challenge? _____

_____

_____

_____

_____

What did I savor today? _____

_____

_____

_____

_____

YEAR ONE

What did I do today? _____

_____

_____

_____

_____

What did I feel today? _____

_____

_____

_____

_____

What am I grateful for today? _____

_____

_____

_____

_____

What challenged me today? _____

_____

_____

_____

_____

How can I overcome that challenge? _____

_____

_____

_____

_____

What did I savor today? _____

_____

_____

_____

_____

YEAR TWO

BUILDING the BEST YOU THERE IS

_____ Date

What did I do today? _____
_____
_____
_____
_____

What did I feel today? _____
_____
_____
_____

What am I grateful for today? _____
_____
_____
_____

What challenged me today? _____
_____
_____
_____

How can I overcome that challenge? _____
_____
_____
_____

What did I savor today? _____
_____
_____
_____

YEAR ONE

_____ Date

What did I do today? _____
_____
_____
_____
_____

What did I feel today? _____
_____
_____
_____

What am I grateful for today? _____
_____
_____
_____

What challenged me today? _____
_____
_____
_____

How can I overcome that challenge? _____
_____
_____
_____

What did I savor today? _____
_____
_____
_____

YEAR TWO

BUILDING _the_ BEST YOU THERE IS

What did I do today? _____

_____

_____

_____

_____

What did I feel today? _____

_____

_____

_____

_____

What am I grateful for today? _____

_____

_____

_____

_____

What challenged me today? _____

_____

_____

_____

_____

How can I overcome that challenge? _____

_____

_____

_____

_____

What did I savor today? _____

_____

_____

_____

_____

What did I do today? _____

_____

_____

_____

_____

What did I feel today? _____

_____

_____

_____

_____

What am I grateful for today? _____

_____

_____

_____

_____

What challenged me today? _____

_____

_____

_____

_____

How can I overcome that challenge? _____

_____

_____

_____

_____

What did I savor today? _____

_____

_____

_____

_____

_____ Date   _____ Date

What did I do today? _____   What did I do today? _____
_____   _____
_____   _____
_____   _____

What did I feel today? _____   What did I feel today? _____
_____   _____
_____   _____
_____   _____

What am I grateful for today? _____   What am I grateful for today? _____
_____   _____
_____   _____
_____   _____

What challenged me today? _____   What challenged me today? _____
_____   _____
_____   _____
_____   _____

How can I overcome that challenge? ___   How can I overcome that challenge? ___
_____   _____
_____   _____
_____   _____

What did I savor today? _____   What did I savor today? _____
_____   _____
_____   _____
_____   _____

BUILDING *the* BEST YOU THERE IS

What did I do today? _____

_____

_____

_____

What did I feel today? _____

_____

_____

_____

What am I grateful for today? _____

_____

_____

_____

What challenged me today? _____

_____

_____

_____

How can I overcome that challenge? _____

_____

_____

_____

What did I savor today? _____

_____

_____

_____

What did I do today? _____

_____

_____

_____

What did I feel today? _____

_____

_____

_____

What am I grateful for today? _____

_____

_____

_____

What challenged me today? _____

_____

_____

_____

How can I overcome that challenge? _____

_____

_____

_____

What did I savor today? _____

_____

_____

_____

_____ Date

What did I do today? _____
_____
_____
_____
_____

What did I feel today? _____
_____
_____
_____
_____

What am I grateful for today? _____
_____
_____
_____
_____

What challenged me today? _____
_____
_____
_____
_____

How can I overcome that challenge? _____
_____
_____
_____
_____

What did I savor today? _____
_____
_____
_____
_____

YEAR ONE

_____ Date

What did I do today? _____
_____
_____
_____
_____

What did I feel today? _____
_____
_____
_____
_____

What am I grateful for today? _____
_____
_____
_____
_____

What challenged me today? _____
_____
_____
_____
_____

How can I overcome that challenge? _____
_____
_____
_____
_____

What did I savor today? _____
_____
_____
_____
_____

YEAR TWO

BUILDING the BEST YOU THERE IS

What did I do today? _____

_____

_____

_____

_____

What did I feel today? _____

_____

_____

_____

_____

What am I grateful for today? _____

_____

_____

_____

_____

What challenged me today? _____

_____

_____

_____

_____

How can I overcome that challenge? _____

_____

_____

_____

_____

What did I savor today? _____

_____

_____

_____

_____

What did I do today? _____

_____

_____

_____

_____

What did I feel today? _____

_____

_____

_____

_____

What am I grateful for today? _____

_____

_____

_____

_____

What challenged me today? _____

_____

_____

_____

_____

How can I overcome that challenge? _____

_____

_____

_____

_____

What did I savor today? _____

_____

_____

_____

_____

BUILDING *the* BEST YOU THERE IS

_____ Date

What did I do today? _____
_____
_____
_____
_____

What did I feel today? _____
_____
_____
_____

What am I grateful for today? _____
_____
_____
_____

What challenged me today? _____
_____
_____
_____

How can I overcome that challenge? _____
_____
_____
_____

What did I savor today? _____
_____
_____
_____
_____

YEAR ONE

_____ Date

What did I do today? _____
_____
_____
_____
_____

What did I feel today? _____
_____
_____
_____

What am I grateful for today? _____
_____
_____
_____

What challenged me today? _____
_____
_____
_____

How can I overcome that challenge? _____
_____
_____
_____

What did I savor today? _____
_____
_____
_____
_____

YEAR TWO

BUILDING _the_ BEST YOU THERE IS

_____ Date

What did I do today? _____

_____

_____

_____

What did I feel today? _____

_____

_____

_____

What am I grateful for today? _____

_____

_____

_____

What challenged me today? _____

_____

_____

_____

How can I overcome that challenge? _____

_____

_____

_____

What did I savor today? _____

_____

_____

_____

YEAR ONE

_____ Date

What did I do today? _____

_____

_____

_____

What did I feel today? _____

_____

_____

_____

What am I grateful for today? _____

_____

_____

_____

What challenged me today? _____

_____

_____

_____

How can I overcome that challenge? _____

_____

_____

_____

What did I savor today? _____

_____

_____

_____

YEAR TWO

BUILDING *the* BEST YOU THERE IS

_____ Date

What did I do today? _____
_____
_____
_____
_____

What did I feel today? _____
_____
_____
_____
_____

What am I grateful for today? _____
_____
_____
_____
_____

What challenged me today? _____
_____
_____
_____
_____

How can I overcome that challenge? _____
_____
_____
_____
_____

What did I savor today? _____
_____
_____
_____
_____

YEAR ONE

_____ Date

What did I do today? _____
_____
_____
_____
_____

What did I feel today? _____
_____
_____
_____
_____

What am I grateful for today? _____
_____
_____
_____
_____

What challenged me today? _____
_____
_____
_____
_____

How can I overcome that challenge? _____
_____
_____
_____
_____

What did I savor today? _____
_____
_____
_____
_____

YEAR TWO

BUILDING *the* BEST YOU THERE IS

_____ Date   _____ Date

What did I do today? _____   *What did I do today?* _____
_____   _____
_____   _____
_____   _____
_____   _____

What did I feel today? _____   *What did I feel today?* _____
_____   _____
_____   _____
_____   _____
_____   _____

What am I grateful for today? _____   *What am I grateful for today?* _____
_____   _____
_____   _____
_____   _____
_____   _____

What challenged me today? _____   *What challenged me today?* _____
_____   _____
_____   _____
_____   _____
_____   _____

How can I overcome that challenge? _____   *How can I overcome that challenge?* _____
_____   _____
_____   _____
_____   _____
_____   _____

What did I savor today? _____   *What did I savor today?* _____
_____   _____
_____   _____
_____   _____

YEAR ONE   YEAR TWO

BUILDING *the* BEST YOU THERE IS

_____ Date

What did I do today? _____
_____
_____
_____
_____

What did I feel today? _____
_____
_____
_____
_____

What am I grateful for today? _____
_____
_____
_____
_____

What challenged me today? _____
_____
_____
_____

How can I overcome that challenge? _____
_____
_____
_____
_____

What did I savor today? _____
_____
_____
_____
_____

YEAR ONE

_____ Date

What did I do today? _____
_____
_____
_____
_____

What did I feel today? _____
_____
_____
_____
_____

What am I grateful for today? _____
_____
_____
_____
_____

What challenged me today? _____
_____
_____
_____

How can I overcome that challenge? _____
_____
_____
_____
_____

What did I savor today? _____
_____
_____
_____
_____

YEAR TWO

BUILDING _the_ BEST YOU THERE IS

                                              _____ Date   _____ Date

What did I do today? _____   What did I do today? _____
_____   _____
_____   _____
_____   _____

What did I feel today? _____   What did I feel today? _____
_____   _____
_____   _____
_____   _____
_____   _____

What am I grateful for today? _____   What am I grateful for today? _____
_____   _____
_____   _____
_____   _____

What challenged me today? _____   What challenged me today? _____
_____   _____
_____   _____
_____   _____

How can I overcome that challenge? _____   How can I overcome that challenge? _____
_____   _____
_____   _____
_____   _____
_____   _____

What did I savor today? _____   What did I savor today? _____
_____   _____
_____   _____
_____   _____

                                        YEAR ONE   YEAR TWO

                              BUILDING *the* BEST YOU THERE IS

_____ Date

What did I do today? _____
_____
_____
_____
_____

What did I feel today? _____
_____
_____
_____
_____

What am I grateful for today? _____
_____
_____
_____
_____

What challenged me today? _____
_____
_____
_____
_____

How can I overcome that challenge? _____
_____
_____
_____
_____

What did I savor today? _____
_____
_____
_____
_____

YEAR ONE

_____ Date

What did I do today? _____
_____
_____
_____
_____

What did I feel today? _____
_____
_____
_____
_____

What am I grateful for today? _____
_____
_____
_____
_____

What challenged me today? _____
_____
_____
_____
_____

How can I overcome that challenge? _____
_____
_____
_____
_____

What did I savor today? _____
_____
_____
_____
_____

YEAR TWO

BUILDING _the_ BEST YOU THERE IS

_____ Date   _____ Date

What did I do today? _____   What did I do today? _____
_____   _____
_____   _____
_____   _____

What did I feel today? _____   What did I feel today? _____
_____   _____
_____   _____
_____   _____

What am I grateful for today? _____   What am I grateful for today? _____
_____   _____
_____   _____
_____   _____

What challenged me today? _____   What challenged me today? _____
_____   _____
_____   _____
_____   _____

How can I overcome that challenge? ___   How can I overcome that challenge? ___
_____   _____
_____   _____
_____   _____
_____   _____

What did I savor today? _____   What did I savor today? _____
_____   _____
_____   _____
_____   _____

YEAR ONE   YEAR TWO

BUILDING *the* BEST YOU THERE IS

_____ Date   _____ Date

What did I do today? _____   What did I do today? _____
_____   _____
_____   _____
_____   _____
_____   _____

What did I feel today? _____   What did I feel today? _____
_____   _____
_____   _____
_____   _____
_____   _____

What am I grateful for today? _____   What am I grateful for today? _____
_____   _____
_____   _____
_____   _____
_____   _____

What challenged me today? _____   What challenged me today? _____
_____   _____
_____   _____
_____   _____
_____   _____

How can I overcome that challenge? _____   How can I overcome that challenge? _____
_____   _____
_____   _____
_____   _____
_____   _____

What did I savor today? _____   What did I savor today? _____
_____   _____
_____   _____
_____   _____
_____   _____

YEAR ONE   YEAR TWO

BUILDING _the_ BEST YOU THERE IS

What did I do today? _____

_____
_____
_____
_____

What did I feel today? _____

_____
_____
_____
_____

What am I grateful for today? _____

_____
_____
_____
_____

What challenged me today? _____

_____
_____
_____
_____

How can I overcome that challenge? _____

_____
_____
_____
_____

What did I savor today? _____

_____
_____
_____
_____

What did I do today? _____

_____
_____
_____
_____

What did I feel today? _____

_____
_____
_____
_____

What am I grateful for today? _____

_____
_____
_____
_____

What challenged me today? _____

_____
_____
_____
_____

How can I overcome that challenge? _____

_____
_____
_____
_____

What did I savor today? _____

_____
_____
_____
_____

YEAR ONE

YEAR TWO

BUILDING *the* BEST YOU THERE IS

_____ Date

What did I do today? _____

_____

_____

_____

_____

What did I feel today? _____

_____

_____

_____

_____

What am I grateful for today? _____

_____

_____

_____

_____

What challenged me today? _____

_____

_____

_____

How can I overcome that challenge? _____

_____

_____

_____

_____

What did I savor today? _____

_____

_____

_____

_____

YEAR ONE

_____ Date

What did I do today? _____

_____

_____

_____

_____

What did I feel today? _____

_____

_____

_____

_____

What am I grateful for today? _____

_____

_____

_____

_____

What challenged me today? _____

_____

_____

_____

How can I overcome that challenge? _____

_____

_____

_____

_____

What did I savor today? _____

_____

_____

_____

_____

YEAR TWO

BUILDING _the_ BEST YOU THERE IS

What did I do today? _____

_____

_____

_____

_____

What did I feel today? _____

_____

_____

_____

_____

What am I grateful for today? _____

_____

_____

_____

_____

What challenged me today? _____

_____

_____

_____

_____

How can I overcome that challenge? ____

_____

_____

_____

_____

What did I savor today? _____

_____

_____

_____

_____

What did I do today? _____

_____

_____

_____

_____

What did I feel today? _____

_____

_____

_____

_____

What am I grateful for today? _____

_____

_____

_____

_____

What challenged me today? _____

_____

_____

_____

_____

How can I overcome that challenge? ____

_____

_____

_____

_____

What did I savor today? _____

_____

_____

_____

_____

BUILDING *the* BEST YOU THERE IS

_____ Date

What did I do today? _____
_____
_____
_____
_____

What did I feel today? _____
_____
_____
_____

What am I grateful for today? _____
_____
_____
_____

What challenged me today? _____
_____
_____
_____

How can I overcome that challenge? _____
_____
_____
_____

What did I savor today? _____
_____
_____
_____

_____ Date

What did I do today? _____
_____
_____
_____
_____

What did I feel today? _____
_____
_____
_____

What am I grateful for today? _____
_____
_____
_____

What challenged me today? _____
_____
_____
_____

How can I overcome that challenge? _____
_____
_____
_____

What did I savor today? _____
_____
_____
_____

_____ Date   _____ Date

What did I do today? _____   *What did I do today?* _____
_____   _____
_____   _____
_____   _____

What did I feel today? _____   *What did I feel today?* _____
_____   _____
_____   _____
_____   _____

What am I grateful for today? _____   *What am I grateful for today?* _____
_____   _____
_____   _____
_____   _____

What challenged me today? _____   *What challenged me today?* _____
_____   _____
_____   _____
_____   _____

How can I overcome that challenge? _____   *How can I overcome that challenge?* _____
_____   _____
_____   _____
_____   _____

What did I savor today? _____   *What did I savor today?* _____
_____   _____
_____   _____
_____   _____

YEAR ONE   YEAR TWO

BUILDING *the* BEST YOU THERE IS

What did I do today? _____   What did I do today? _____

_____   _____
_____   _____
_____   _____
_____   _____

What did I feel today? _____   What did I feel today? _____

_____   _____
_____   _____
_____   _____
_____   _____

What am I grateful for today? _____   What am I grateful for today? _____

_____   _____
_____   _____
_____   _____
_____   _____

What challenged me today? _____   What challenged me today? _____

_____   _____
_____   _____
_____   _____
_____   _____

How can I overcome that challenge? _____   How can I overcome that challenge? _____

_____   _____
_____   _____
_____   _____
_____   _____

What did I savor today? _____   What did I savor today? _____

_____   _____
_____   _____
_____   _____
_____   _____

YEAR ONE   YEAR TWO

BUILDING *the* BEST YOU THERE IS

_____ Date   _____ Date

What did I do today? _____   *What did I do today?* _____
_____   _____
_____   _____
_____   _____
_____   _____

What did I feel today? _____   *What did I feel today?* _____
_____   _____
_____   _____
_____   _____
_____   _____

What am I grateful for today? _____   *What am I grateful for today?* _____
_____   _____
_____   _____
_____   _____
_____   _____

What challenged me today? _____   *What challenged me today?* _____
_____   _____
_____   _____
_____   _____
_____   _____

How can I overcome that challenge? _____ *How can I overcome that challenge?* _____
_____   _____
_____   _____
_____   _____
_____   _____

What did I savor today? _____   *What did I savor today?* _____
_____   _____
_____   _____
_____   _____
_____   _____

YEAR ONE   YEAR TWO

BUILDING *the* BEST YOU THERE IS

_____ Date

What did I do today? _____
_____
_____
_____
_____

What did I feel today? _____
_____
_____
_____
_____

What am I grateful for today? _____
_____
_____
_____
_____

What challenged me today? _____
_____
_____
_____
_____

How can I overcome that challenge? ___
_____
_____
_____
_____

What did I savor today? _____
_____
_____
_____
_____

YEAR ONE

_____ Date

What did I do today? _____
_____
_____
_____
_____

What did I feel today? _____
_____
_____
_____
_____

What am I grateful for today? _____
_____
_____
_____
_____

What challenged me today? _____
_____
_____
_____
_____

How can I overcome that challenge? ___
_____
_____
_____
_____

What did I savor today? _____
_____
_____
_____
_____

YEAR TWO

BUILDING _the_ BEST YOU THERE IS

_____ Date   _____ Date

What did I do today? _____   What did I do today? _____
_____   _____
_____   _____
_____   _____
_____   _____

What did I feel today? _____   What did I feel today? _____
_____   _____
_____   _____
_____   _____
_____   _____

What am I grateful for today? _____   What am I grateful for today? _____
_____   _____
_____   _____
_____   _____
_____   _____

What challenged me today? _____   What challenged me today? _____
_____   _____
_____   _____
_____   _____

How can I overcome that challenge? _____   How can I overcome that challenge? _____
_____   _____
_____   _____
_____   _____

What did I savor today? _____   What did I savor today? _____
_____   _____
_____   _____
_____   _____

YEAR ONE   YEAR TWO

BUILDING _the_ BEST YOU THERE IS

_____ _Date_

What did I do today? _____

_____

_____

_____

_____

What did I feel today? _____

_____

_____

_____

_____

What am I grateful for today? _____

_____

_____

_____

What challenged me today? _____

_____

_____

_____

_____

How can I overcome that challenge? _____

_____

_____

_____

_____

What did I savor today? _____

_____

_____

_____

_____

YEAR ONE

_____ _Date_

What did I do today? _____

_____

_____

_____

_____

What did I feel today? _____

_____

_____

_____

_____

What am I grateful for today? _____

_____

_____

_____

What challenged me today? _____

_____

_____

_____

_____

How can I overcome that challenge? _____

_____

_____

_____

_____

What did I savor today? _____

_____

_____

_____

_____

YEAR TWO

BUILDING _the_ BEST YOU THERE IS

_____ Date

What did I do today? _____
_____
_____
_____
_____

What did I feel today? _____
_____
_____
_____
_____

What am I grateful for today? _____
_____
_____
_____
_____

What challenged me today? _____
_____
_____
_____
_____

How can I overcome that challenge? ___
_____
_____
_____
_____

What did I savor today? _____
_____
_____
_____
_____

YEAR ONE

_____ Date

What did I do today? _____
_____
_____
_____
_____

What did I feel today? _____
_____
_____
_____
_____

What am I grateful for today? _____
_____
_____
_____
_____

What challenged me today? _____
_____
_____
_____
_____

How can I overcome that challenge? ___
_____
_____
_____
_____

What did I savor today? _____
_____
_____
_____
_____

YEAR TWO

BUILDING _the_ BEST YOU THERE IS

_____ Date

What did I do today? _____
_____
_____
_____
_____

What did I feel today? _____
_____
_____
_____
_____

What am I grateful for today? _____
_____
_____
_____
_____

What challenged me today? _____
_____
_____
_____

How can I overcome that challenge? _____
_____
_____
_____
_____

What did I savor today? _____
_____
_____
_____
_____

YEAR ONE

_____ Date

What did I do today? _____
_____
_____
_____
_____

What did I feel today? _____
_____
_____
_____
_____

What am I grateful for today? _____
_____
_____
_____
_____

What challenged me today? _____
_____
_____
_____

How can I overcome that challenge? _____
_____
_____
_____
_____

What did I savor today? _____
_____
_____
_____
_____

YEAR TWO

BUILDING _the_ BEST YOU THERE IS

_____ Date

What did I do today? _____
_____
_____
_____
_____

What did I feel today? _____
_____
_____
_____
_____

What am I grateful for today? _____
_____
_____
_____
_____

What challenged me today? _____
_____
_____
_____
_____

How can I overcome that challenge? _____
_____
_____
_____
_____

What did I savor today? _____
_____
_____
_____
_____

YEAR ONE

_____ Date

What did I do today? _____
_____
_____
_____
_____

What did I feel today? _____
_____
_____
_____
_____

What am I grateful for today? _____
_____
_____
_____
_____

What challenged me today? _____
_____
_____
_____
_____

How can I overcome that challenge? _____
_____
_____
_____
_____

What did I savor today? _____
_____
_____
_____
_____

YEAR TWO

BUILDING *the* BEST YOU THERE IS

_____ Date	_____ Date
What did I do today? _____	*What did I do today?* _____
_____	_____
_____	_____
_____	_____
_____	_____
What did I feel today? _____	*What did I feel today?* _____
_____	_____
_____	_____
_____	_____
What am I grateful for today? _____	*What am I grateful for today?* _____
_____	_____
_____	_____
_____	_____
_____	_____
What challenged me today? _____	*What challenged me today?* _____
_____	_____
_____	_____
_____	_____
How can I overcome that challenge? ___	*How can I overcome that challenge?* ___
_____	_____
_____	_____
_____	_____
_____	_____
What did I savor today? _____	*What did I savor today?* _____
_____	_____
_____	_____
_____	_____
YEAR ONE	YEAR TWO

BUILDING *the* BEST YOU THERE IS

| | Date _____ | | Date _____ |

What did I do today? _____

_____

_____

_____

_____

What did I feel today? _____

_____

_____

_____

_____

What am I grateful for today? _____

_____

_____

_____

_____

What challenged me today? _____

_____

_____

_____

_____

How can I overcome that challenge? _____

_____

_____

_____

_____

What did I savor today? _____

_____

_____

_____

_____

What did I do today? _____

_____

_____

_____

_____

What did I feel today? _____

_____

_____

_____

_____

What am I grateful for today? _____

_____

_____

_____

_____

What challenged me today? _____

_____

_____

_____

_____

How can I overcome that challenge? _____

_____

_____

_____

_____

What did I savor today? _____

_____

_____

_____

_____

YEAR ONE

YEAR TWO

BUILDING *the* BEST YOU THERE IS

_____ Date

What did I do today? _____
_____
_____
_____
_____

What did I feel today? _____
_____
_____
_____
_____

What am I grateful for today? _____
_____
_____
_____
_____

What challenged me today? _____
_____
_____
_____
_____

How can I overcome that challenge? _____
_____
_____
_____
_____

What did I savor today? _____
_____
_____
_____
_____

YEAR ONE

_____ Date

What did I do today? _____
_____
_____
_____
_____

What did I feel today? _____
_____
_____
_____
_____

What am I grateful for today? _____
_____
_____
_____
_____

What challenged me today? _____
_____
_____
_____
_____

How can I overcome that challenge? _____
_____
_____
_____
_____

What did I savor today? _____
_____
_____
_____
_____

YEAR TWO

BUILDING _the_ BEST YOU THERE IS

———— Date ————

What did I do today? _____

_____

_____

_____

What did I feel today? _____

_____

_____

_____

What am I grateful for today? _____

_____

_____

_____

What challenged me today? _____

_____

_____

_____

How can I overcome that challenge? _____

_____

_____

_____

What did I savor today? _____

_____

_____

_____

———— Date ————

What did I do today? _____

_____

_____

_____

What did I feel today? _____

_____

_____

_____

What am I grateful for today? _____

_____

_____

_____

What challenged me today? _____

_____

_____

_____

How can I overcome that challenge? _____

_____

_____

_____

What did I savor today? _____

_____

_____

_____

YEAR ONE

YEAR TWO

BUILDING *the* BEST YOU THERE IS

_____ Date

What did I do today? _____
_____
_____
_____
_____

What did I feel today? _____
_____
_____
_____
_____

What am I grateful for today? _____
_____
_____
_____
_____

What challenged me today? _____
_____
_____
_____
_____

How can I overcome that challenge? _____
_____
_____
_____
_____

What did I savor today? _____
_____
_____
_____
_____

YEAR ONE

_____ Date

What did I do today? _____
_____
_____
_____
_____

What did I feel today? _____
_____
_____
_____
_____

What am I grateful for today? _____
_____
_____
_____
_____

What challenged me today? _____
_____
_____
_____
_____

How can I overcome that challenge? _____
_____
_____
_____
_____

What did I savor today? _____
_____
_____
_____
_____

YEAR TWO

BUILDING *the* BEST YOU THERE IS

What did I do today? _____

_____

_____

_____

_____

What did I feel today? _____

_____

_____

_____

_____

What am I grateful for today? _____

_____

_____

_____

_____

What challenged me today? _____

_____

_____

_____

_____

How can I overcome that challenge? _____

_____

_____

_____

_____

What did I savor today? _____

_____

_____

_____

_____

YEAR ONE

What did I do today? _____

_____

_____

_____

_____

What did I feel today? _____

_____

_____

_____

_____

What am I grateful for today? _____

_____

_____

_____

_____

What challenged me today? _____

_____

_____

_____

_____

How can I overcome that challenge? _____

_____

_____

_____

_____

What did I savor today? _____

_____

_____

_____

_____

YEAR TWO

_____ Date

What did I do today? _____
_____
_____
_____
_____

What did I feel today? _____
_____
_____
_____
_____

What am I grateful for today? _____
_____
_____
_____
_____

What challenged me today? _____
_____
_____
_____
_____

How can I overcome that challenge? _____
_____
_____
_____
_____

What did I savor today? _____
_____
_____
_____
_____

YEAR ONE

_____ Date

What did I do today? _____
_____
_____
_____
_____

What did I feel today? _____
_____
_____
_____
_____

What am I grateful for today? _____
_____
_____
_____
_____

What challenged me today? _____
_____
_____
_____
_____

How can I overcome that challenge? _____
_____
_____
_____
_____

What did I savor today? _____
_____
_____
_____
_____

YEAR TWO

BUILDING _the_ BEST YOU THERE IS

_____ Date

What did I do today? _____
_____
_____
_____
_____

What did I feel today? _____
_____
_____
_____

What am I grateful for today? _____
_____
_____
_____

What challenged me today? _____
_____
_____
_____

How can I overcome that challenge? ____
_____
_____
_____
_____

What did I savor today? _____
_____
_____
_____

YEAR ONE

_____ Date

What did I do today? _____
_____
_____
_____
_____

What did I feel today? _____
_____
_____
_____

What am I grateful for today? _____
_____
_____
_____

What challenged me today? _____
_____
_____
_____

How can I overcome that challenge? ____
_____
_____
_____
_____

What did I savor today? _____
_____
_____
_____

YEAR TWO

BUILDING _the_ BEST YOU THERE IS

_____ Date

What did I do today? _____
_____
_____
_____
_____

What did I feel today? _____
_____
_____
_____
_____

What am I grateful for today? _____
_____
_____
_____
_____

What challenged me today? _____
_____
_____
_____
_____

How can I overcome that challenge? _____
_____
_____
_____
_____

What did I savor today? _____
_____
_____
_____
_____

YEAR ONE

_____ Date

What did I do today? _____
_____
_____
_____
_____

What did I feel today? _____
_____
_____
_____
_____

What am I grateful for today? _____
_____
_____
_____
_____

What challenged me today? _____
_____
_____
_____
_____

How can I overcome that challenge? _____
_____
_____
_____
_____

What did I savor today? _____
_____
_____
_____
_____

YEAR TWO

_____ Date

What did I do today? _____

_____
_____
_____
_____

What did I feel today? _____

_____
_____
_____
_____

What am I grateful for today? _____

_____
_____
_____
_____

What challenged me today? _____

_____
_____
_____
_____

How can I overcome that challenge? _____

_____
_____
_____
_____

What did I savor today? _____

_____
_____
_____
_____

YEAR ONE

_____ Date

What did I do today? _____

_____
_____
_____
_____

What did I feel today? _____

_____
_____
_____
_____

What am I grateful for today? _____

_____
_____
_____
_____

What challenged me today? _____

_____
_____
_____
_____

How can I overcome that challenge? _____

_____
_____
_____
_____

What did I savor today? _____

_____
_____
_____
_____

YEAR TWO

BUILDING *the* BEST YOU THERE IS

What did I do today? _____

What did I do today? _____

_____

_____

_____

_____

_____

_____

_____

_____

What did I feel today? _____

What did I feel today? _____

_____

_____

_____

_____

_____

_____

What am I grateful for today? _____

What am I grateful for today? _____

_____

_____

_____

_____

_____

_____

What challenged me today? _____

What challenged me today? _____

_____

_____

_____

_____

_____

_____

How can I overcome that challenge? _____

How can I overcome that challenge? _____

_____

_____

_____

_____

_____

_____

What did I savor today? _____

What did I savor today? _____

_____

_____

_____

_____

_____

_____

_____

_____

BUILDING *the* BEST YOU THERE IS

_____ Date   _____ Date

What did I do today? _____   *What did I do today?* _____
_____   _____
_____   _____
_____   _____
_____   _____

What did I feel today? _____   *What did I feel today?* _____
_____   _____
_____   _____
_____   _____
_____   _____

What am I grateful for today? _____   *What am I grateful for today?* _____
_____   _____
_____   _____
_____   _____
_____   _____

What challenged me today? _____   *What challenged me today?* _____
_____   _____
_____   _____
_____   _____
_____   _____

How can I overcome that challenge? _____   *How can I overcome that challenge?* _____
_____   _____
_____   _____
_____   _____
_____   _____

What did I savor today? _____   *What did I savor today?* _____
_____   _____
_____   _____
_____   _____

YEAR ONE   YEAR TWO

BUILDING *the* BEST YOU THERE IS

_____ Date

What did I do today? _____

_____
_____
_____
_____

What did I feel today? _____

_____
_____
_____
_____

What am I grateful for today? _____

_____
_____
_____
_____

What challenged me today? _____

_____
_____
_____
_____

How can I overcome that challenge? _____

_____
_____
_____
_____

What did I savor today? _____

_____
_____
_____
_____

YEAR ONE

_____ Date

What did I do today? _____

_____
_____
_____
_____

What did I feel today? _____

_____
_____
_____
_____

What am I grateful for today? _____

_____
_____
_____
_____

What challenged me today? _____

_____
_____
_____
_____

How can I overcome that challenge? _____

_____
_____
_____
_____

What did I savor today? _____

_____
_____
_____
_____

YEAR TWO

BUILDING _the_ BEST YOU THERE IS

Do I feel loved? _____

_____

_____

_____

_____

Do I rely on others for love? _____

_____

_____

_____

_____

Am I in search of deeper love? _____

_____

_____

_____

_____

Do I know how to achieve deep love? _____

_____

_____

_____

_____

Am I in touch with my feelings? _____

_____

_____

_____

_____

What would bring me more love? _____

_____

_____

_____

_____

Do I believe in havingness? _____
_____
_____
_____
_____

Am I creating prosperity? _____
_____
_____
_____
_____

Could my life be easier? _____
_____
_____
_____
_____

What can I do to make it easier? _____
_____
_____
_____
_____

Do I have everything I need? _____
_____
_____
_____
_____

Do I have everything I want? _____
_____
_____
_____
_____

BUILDING *the* BEST YOU THERE IS

Do I feel loved? _____

_____

_____

_____

_____

Do I rely on others for love? _____

_____

_____

_____

_____

Am I in search of deeper love? _____

_____

_____

_____

_____

Do I know how to achieve deep love? _____

_____

_____

_____

_____

Am I in touch with my feelings? _____

_____

_____

_____

_____

What would bring me more love? _____

_____

_____

_____

_____

BUILDING *the* BEST YOU THERE IS

WO

Do I believe in havingness? _____

_____
_____
_____

Am I creating prosperity? _____

_____
_____
_____

Could my life be easier? _____

_____
_____
_____

What can I do to make it easier? _____

_____
_____
_____

Do I have everything I need? _____

_____
_____
_____

Do I have everything I want? _____

_____
_____
_____

 BUILDING *the* BEST YOU THERE IS

_____ Date

What did I do today? _____

_____

_____

_____

What did I feel today? _____

_____

_____

_____

What am I grateful for today? _____

_____

_____

_____

What challenged me today? _____

_____

_____

_____

How can I overcome that challenge? _____

_____

_____

_____

What did I savor today? _____

_____

_____

_____

YEAR ONE

_____ Date

What did I do today? _____

_____

_____

_____

What did I feel today? _____

_____

_____

_____

What am I grateful for today? _____

_____

_____

_____

What challenged me today? _____

_____

_____

_____

How can I overcome that challenge? _____

_____

_____

_____

What did I savor today? _____

_____

_____

_____

YEAR TWO

BUILDING *the* BEST YOU THERE IS

Date _____

What did I do today? _____
_____
_____
_____

What did I feel today? _____
_____
_____
_____

What am I grateful for today? _____
_____
_____
_____

What challenged me today? _____
_____
_____
_____

How can I overcome that challenge? _____
_____
_____
_____

What did I savor today? _____
_____
_____
_____

YEAR ONE

Date _____

What did I do today? _____
_____
_____
_____

What did I feel today? _____
_____
_____
_____

What am I grateful for today? _____
_____
_____
_____

What challenged me today? _____
_____
_____
_____

How can I overcome that challenge? _____
_____
_____
_____

What did I savor today? _____
_____
_____
_____

YEAR TWO

BUILDING _the_ BEST YOU THERE IS

What did I do today? _____   What did I do today? _____
_____   _____
_____   _____
_____   _____
_____   _____

What did I feel today? _____   What did I feel today? _____
_____   _____
_____   _____
_____   _____
_____   _____

What am I grateful for today? _____   What am I grateful for today? _____
_____   _____
_____   _____
_____   _____
_____   _____

What challenged me today? _____   What challenged me today? _____
_____   _____
_____   _____
_____   _____
_____   _____

How can I overcome that challenge? _____   How can I overcome that challenge? _____
_____   _____
_____   _____
_____   _____
_____   _____

What did I savor today? _____   What did I savor today? _____
_____   _____
_____   _____
_____   _____

BUILDING *the* BEST YOU THERE IS

_____ Date

What did I do today? _____

_____

_____

_____

_____

What did I feel today? _____

_____

_____

_____

_____

What am I grateful for today? _____

_____

_____

_____

_____

What challenged me today? _____

_____

_____

_____

_____

How can I overcome that challenge? _____

_____

_____

_____

_____

What did I savor today? _____

_____

_____

_____

_____

YEAR ONE

_____ Date

What did I do today? _____

_____

_____

_____

_____

What did I feel today? _____

_____

_____

_____

_____

What am I grateful for today? _____

_____

_____

_____

_____

What challenged me today? _____

_____

_____

_____

_____

How can I overcome that challenge? _____

_____

_____

_____

_____

What did I savor today? _____

_____

_____

_____

_____

YEAR TWO

BUILDING _the_ BEST YOU THERE IS

What did I do today? _____

_____

_____

_____

What did I feel today? _____

_____

_____

_____

What am I grateful for today? _____

_____

_____

_____

What challenged me today? _____

_____

_____

_____

How can I overcome that challenge? _____

_____

_____

_____

What did I savor today? _____

_____

_____

_____

What did I do today? _____

_____

_____

_____

What did I feel today? _____

_____

_____

_____

What am I grateful for today? _____

_____

_____

_____

What challenged me today? _____

_____

_____

_____

How can I overcome that challenge? _____

_____

_____

_____

What did I savor today? _____

_____

_____

_____

_____ Date

What did I do today? _____
_____
_____
_____

What did I feel today? _____
_____
_____
_____

What am I grateful for today? _____
_____
_____
_____

What challenged me today? _____
_____
_____
_____

How can I overcome that challenge? _____
_____
_____
_____

What did I savor today? _____
_____
_____
_____

YEAR ONE

_____ Date

What did I do today? _____
_____
_____
_____

What did I feel today? _____
_____
_____
_____

What am I grateful for today? _____
_____
_____
_____

What challenged me today? _____
_____
_____
_____

How can I overcome that challenge? _____
_____
_____
_____

What did I savor today? _____
_____
_____
_____

YEAR TWO

BUILDING *the* BEST YOU THERE IS

_____ *Date*

What did I do today? _____

_____
_____
_____

What did I feel today? _____

_____
_____
_____

What am I grateful for today? _____

_____
_____
_____

What challenged me today? _____

_____
_____
_____

How can I overcome that challenge? _____

_____
_____
_____

What did I savor today? _____

_____
_____
_____

YEAR ONE

_____ *Date*

What did I do today? _____

_____
_____
_____

What did I feel today? _____

_____
_____
_____

What am I grateful for today? _____

_____
_____
_____

What challenged me today? _____

_____
_____
_____

How can I overcome that challenge? _____

_____
_____
_____

What did I savor today? _____

_____
_____
_____

YEAR TWO

BUILDING *the* BEST YOU THERE IS

Date	Date

What did I do today? _____

_____

_____

_____

_____

What did I feel today? _____

_____

_____

_____

What am I grateful for today? _____

_____

_____

_____

What challenged me today? _____

_____

_____

_____

How can I overcome that challenge? _____

_____

_____

_____

What did I savor today? _____

_____

_____

_____

What did I do today? _____

_____

_____

_____

_____

What did I feel today? _____

_____

_____

_____

What am I grateful for today? _____

_____

_____

_____

What challenged me today? _____

_____

_____

_____

How can I overcome that challenge? _____

_____

_____

_____

What did I savor today? _____

_____

_____

_____

YEAR ONE   YEAR TWO

BUILDING *the* BEST YOU THERE IS

_____ Date   _____ Date

What did I do today? _____   What did I do today? _____
_____   _____
_____   _____
_____   _____
_____   _____

What did I feel today? _____   What did I feel today? _____
_____   _____
_____   _____
_____   _____
_____   _____

What am I grateful for today? _____   What am I grateful for today? _____
_____   _____
_____   _____
_____   _____
_____   _____

What challenged me today? _____   What challenged me today? _____
_____   _____
_____   _____
_____   _____
_____   _____

How can I overcome that challenge? ____   How can I overcome that challenge? ____
_____   _____
_____   _____
_____   _____
_____   _____

What did I savor today? _____   What did I savor today? _____
_____   _____
_____   _____
_____   _____
_____   _____

                          YEAR ONE   YEAR TWO

BUILDING _the_ BEST YOU THERE IS

What did I do today? _____

What did I do today? _____

_____

_____

_____

_____

_____

_____

_____

_____

What did I feel today? _____

What did I feel today? _____

_____

_____

_____

_____

_____

_____

_____

_____

What am I grateful for today? _____

What am I grateful for today? _____

_____

_____

_____

_____

_____

_____

_____

_____

What challenged me today? _____

What challenged me today? _____

_____

_____

_____

_____

_____

_____

_____

_____

How can I overcome that challenge? _____

How can I overcome that challenge? _____

_____

_____

_____

_____

_____

_____

_____

_____

What did I savor today? _____

What did I savor today? _____

_____

_____

_____

_____

_____

_____

_____

_____

YEAR ONE

YEAR TWO

BUILDING *the* BEST YOU THERE IS

_____ Date

What did I do today? _____
_____
_____
_____
_____

What did I feel today? _____
_____
_____
_____
_____

What am I grateful for today? _____
_____
_____
_____
_____

What challenged me today? _____
_____
_____
_____
_____

How can I overcome that challenge? _____
_____
_____
_____
_____

What did I savor today? _____
_____
_____
_____
_____

YEAR ONE

_____ Date

What did I do today? _____
_____
_____
_____
_____

What did I feel today? _____
_____
_____
_____
_____

What am I grateful for today? _____
_____
_____
_____
_____

What challenged me today? _____
_____
_____
_____
_____

How can I overcome that challenge? _____
_____
_____
_____
_____

What did I savor today? _____
_____
_____
_____
_____

YEAR TWO

BUILDING *the* BEST YOU THERE IS

_____ Date

What did I do today? _____

_____

_____

_____

What did I feel today? _____

_____

_____

_____

What am I grateful for today? _____

_____

_____

_____

What challenged me today? _____

_____

_____

_____

How can I overcome that challenge? _____

_____

_____

_____

What did I savor today? _____

_____

_____

_____

YEAR ONE

_____ Date

What did I do today? _____

_____

_____

_____

What did I feel today? _____

_____

_____

_____

What am I grateful for today? _____

_____

_____

_____

What challenged me today? _____

_____

_____

_____

How can I overcome that challenge? _____

_____

_____

_____

What did I savor today? _____

_____

_____

_____

YEAR TWO

BUILDING the BEST YOU THERE IS

_____ Date   _____ Date

What did I do today? _____   *What did I do today?* _____
_____   _____
_____   _____
_____   _____
_____   _____

What did I feel today? _____   *What did I feel today?* _____
_____   _____
_____   _____
_____   _____
_____   _____

What am I grateful for today? _____   *What am I grateful for today?* _____
_____   _____
_____   _____
_____   _____
_____   _____

What challenged me today? _____   *What challenged me today?* _____
_____   _____
_____   _____
_____   _____
_____   _____

How can I overcome that challenge? _____ *How can I overcome that challenge?* _____
_____   _____
_____   _____
_____   _____
_____   _____

What did I savor today? _____   *What did I savor today?* _____
_____   _____
_____   _____
_____   _____
_____   _____

YEAR ONE   YEAR TWO

BUILDING *the* BEST YOU THERE IS

_____ Date

What did I do today? _____

_____

_____

_____

_____

What did I feel today? _____

_____

_____

_____

_____

What am I grateful for today? _____

_____

_____

_____

_____

What challenged me today? _____

_____

_____

_____

How can I overcome that challenge? _____

_____

_____

_____

_____

What did I savor today? _____

_____

_____

_____

_____

YEAR ONE

_____ Date

What did I do today? _____

_____

_____

_____

_____

What did I feel today? _____

_____

_____

_____

_____

What am I grateful for today? _____

_____

_____

_____

_____

What challenged me today? _____

_____

_____

_____

How can I overcome that challenge? _____

_____

_____

_____

_____

What did I savor today? _____

_____

_____

_____

_____

YEAR TWO

BUILDING the BEST YOU THERE IS

_____ Date

What did I do today? _____

_____

_____

_____

What did I feel today? _____

_____

_____

_____

What am I grateful for today? _____

_____

_____

_____

What challenged me today? _____

_____

_____

_____

How can I overcome that challenge? ____

_____

_____

_____

What did I savor today? _____

_____

_____

_____

_____ Date

What did I do today? _____

_____

_____

_____

What did I feel today? _____

_____

_____

_____

What am I grateful for today? _____

_____

_____

_____

What challenged me today? _____

_____

_____

_____

How can I overcome that challenge? ____

_____

_____

_____

What did I savor today? _____

_____

_____

_____

YEAR ONE

YEAR TWO

BUILDING _the_ BEST YOU THERE IS

_____ Date

What did I do today? _____
_____
_____
_____
_____

What did I feel today? _____
_____
_____
_____

What am I grateful for today? _____
_____
_____
_____
_____

What challenged me today? _____
_____
_____
_____
_____

How can I overcome that challenge? _____
_____
_____
_____
_____

What did I savor today? _____
_____
_____
_____
_____

YEAR ONE

_____ Date

What did I do today? _____
_____
_____
_____
_____

What did I feel today? _____
_____
_____
_____

What am I grateful for today? _____
_____
_____
_____
_____

What challenged me today? _____
_____
_____
_____
_____

How can I overcome that challenge? _____
_____
_____
_____
_____

What did I savor today? _____
_____
_____
_____
_____

YEAR TWO

BUILDING _the_ BEST YOU THERE IS

What did I do today? _____

_____

_____

_____

_____

What did I feel today? _____

_____

_____

_____

_____

What am I grateful for today? _____

_____

_____

_____

_____

What challenged me today? _____

_____

_____

_____

_____

How can I overcome that challenge? _____

_____

_____

_____

_____

What did I savor today? _____

_____

_____

_____

What did I do today? _____

_____

_____

_____

_____

What did I feel today? _____

_____

_____

_____

_____

What am I grateful for today? _____

_____

_____

_____

_____

What challenged me today? _____

_____

_____

_____

_____

How can I overcome that challenge? _____

_____

_____

_____

_____

What did I savor today? _____

_____

_____

_____

YEAR ONE

YEAR TWO

BUILDING *the* BEST YOU THERE IS

What did I do today? _____

_____

_____

_____

_____

What did I feel today? _____

_____

_____

_____

_____

What am I grateful for today? _____

_____

_____

_____

_____

What challenged me today? _____

_____

_____

_____

_____

How can I overcome that challenge? _____

_____

_____

_____

_____

What did I savor today? _____

_____

_____

_____

_____

What did I do today? _____

_____

_____

_____

_____

What did I feel today? _____

_____

_____

_____

_____

What am I grateful for today? _____

_____

_____

_____

_____

What challenged me today? _____

_____

_____

_____

_____

How can I overcome that challenge? _____

_____

_____

_____

_____

What did I savor today? _____

_____

_____

_____

_____

_____ Date

What did I do today? _____

_____

_____

_____

_____

What did I feel today? _____

_____

_____

_____

_____

What am I grateful for today? _____

_____

_____

_____

_____

What challenged me today? _____

_____

_____

_____

_____

How can I overcome that challenge? _____

_____

_____

_____

_____

What did I savor today? _____

_____

_____

_____

YEAR ONE

_____ Date

What did I do today? _____

_____

_____

_____

_____

What did I feel today? _____

_____

_____

_____

_____

What am I grateful for today? _____

_____

_____

_____

_____

What challenged me today? _____

_____

_____

_____

_____

How can I overcome that challenge? _____

_____

_____

_____

_____

What did I savor today? _____

_____

_____

_____

YEAR TWO

BUILDING _the_ BEST YOU THERE IS

What did I do today? _____

_____

_____

_____

What did I feel today? _____

_____

_____

_____

What am I grateful for today? _____

_____

_____

_____

What challenged me today? _____

_____

_____

_____

How can I overcome that challenge? _____

_____

_____

_____

What did I savor today? _____

_____

_____

_____

What did I do today? _____

_____

_____

_____

What did I feel today? _____

_____

_____

_____

What am I grateful for today? _____

_____

_____

_____

What challenged me today? _____

_____

_____

_____

How can I overcome that challenge? _____

_____

_____

_____

What did I savor today? _____

_____

_____

_____

_____ Date | _____ Date

What did I do today? _____ | What did I do today? _____

_____ | _____
_____ | _____
_____ | _____
_____ | _____

What did I feel today? _____ | What did I feel today? _____

_____ | _____
_____ | _____
_____ | _____
_____ | _____

What am I grateful for today? _____ | What am I grateful for today? _____

_____ | _____
_____ | _____
_____ | _____
_____ | _____

What challenged me today? _____ | What challenged me today? _____

_____ | _____
_____ | _____
_____ | _____
_____ | _____

How can I overcome that challenge? _____ | How can I overcome that challenge? _____

_____ | _____
_____ | _____
_____ | _____
_____ | _____

What did I savor today? _____ | What did I savor today? _____

_____ | _____
_____ | _____
_____ | _____

YEAR ONE | YEAR TWO

BUILDING _the_ BEST YOU THERE IS

What did I do today? _____

What did I feel today? _____

What am I grateful for today? _____

What challenged me today? _____

How can I overcome that challenge? _____

What did I savor today? _____

What did I do today? _____

What did I feel today? _____

What am I grateful for today? _____

What challenged me today? _____

How can I overcome that challenge? _____

What did I savor today? _____

YEAR ONE

YEAR TWO

BUILDING *the* BEST YOU THERE IS

_____ Date

What did I do today? _____

_____

_____

_____

What did I feel today? _____

_____

_____

_____

What am I grateful for today? _____

_____

_____

_____

What challenged me today? _____

_____

_____

_____

How can I overcome that challenge? ____

_____

_____

_____

What did I savor today? _____

_____

_____

_____

YEAR ONE

_____ Date

What did I do today? _____

_____

_____

_____

What did I feel today? _____

_____

_____

_____

What am I grateful for today? _____

_____

_____

_____

What challenged me today? _____

_____

_____

_____

How can I overcome that challenge? ____

_____

_____

_____

What did I savor today? _____

_____

_____

_____

YEAR TWO

BUILDING _the_ BEST YOU THERE IS

_____ Date

What did I do today? _____

_____

_____

_____

_____

What did I feel today? _____

_____

_____

_____

_____

What am I grateful for today? _____

_____

_____

_____

_____

What challenged me today? _____

_____

_____

_____

_____

How can I overcome that challenge? _____

_____

_____

_____

_____

What did I savor today? _____

_____

_____

_____

_____

YEAR ONE

_____ Date

What did I do today? _____

_____

_____

_____

_____

What did I feel today? _____

_____

_____

_____

_____

What am I grateful for today? _____

_____

_____

_____

_____

What challenged me today? _____

_____

_____

_____

_____

How can I overcome that challenge? _____

_____

_____

_____

_____

What did I savor today? _____

_____

_____

_____

_____

YEAR TWO

BUILDING *the* BEST YOU THERE IS

What did I do today? _____

_____

_____

_____

What did I feel today? _____

_____

_____

_____

What am I grateful for today? _____

_____

_____

_____

What challenged me today? _____

_____

_____

_____

How can I overcome that challenge? _____

_____

_____

_____

What did I savor today? _____

_____

_____

_____

What did I do today? _____

_____

_____

_____

What did I feel today? _____

_____

_____

_____

What am I grateful for today? _____

_____

_____

_____

What challenged me today? _____

_____

_____

_____

How can I overcome that challenge? _____

_____

_____

_____

What did I savor today? _____

_____

_____

_____

YEAR ONE   YEAR TWO

BUILDING *the* BEST YOU THERE IS

_____ Date

What did I do today? _____
_____
_____
_____
_____

What did I feel today? _____
_____
_____
_____

What am I grateful for today? _____
_____
_____
_____

What challenged me today? _____
_____
_____
_____

How can I overcome that challenge? _____
_____
_____
_____

What did I savor today? _____
_____
_____
_____

YEAR ONE

_____ Date

What did I do today? _____
_____
_____
_____
_____

What did I feel today? _____
_____
_____
_____

What am I grateful for today? _____
_____
_____
_____

What challenged me today? _____
_____
_____
_____

How can I overcome that challenge? _____
_____
_____
_____

What did I savor today? _____
_____
_____
_____

YEAR TWO

BUILDING _the_ BEST YOU THERE IS

_____ Date   _____ Date

What did I do today? _____   *What did I do today?* _____
_____   _____
_____   _____
_____   _____
_____   _____

What did I feel today? _____   *What did I feel today?* _____
_____   _____
_____   _____
_____   _____
_____   _____

What am I grateful for today? _____   *What am I grateful for today?* _____
_____   _____
_____   _____
_____   _____
_____   _____

What challenged me today? _____   *What challenged me today?* _____
_____   _____
_____   _____
_____   _____
_____   _____

How can I overcome that challenge? _____   *How can I overcome that challenge?* _____
_____   _____
_____   _____
_____   _____
_____   _____

What did I savor today? _____   *What did I savor today?* _____
_____   _____
_____   _____
_____   _____
_____   _____

YEAR ONE   YEAR TWO

BUILDING *the* BEST YOU THERE IS

_____ Date

What did I do today? _____
_____
_____
_____
_____

What did I feel today? _____
_____
_____
_____
_____

What am I grateful for today? _____
_____
_____
_____
_____

What challenged me today? _____
_____
_____
_____
_____

How can I overcome that challenge? _____
_____
_____
_____
_____

What did I savor today? _____
_____
_____
_____

_____ Date

What did I do today? _____
_____
_____
_____
_____

What did I feel today? _____
_____
_____
_____
_____

What am I grateful for today? _____
_____
_____
_____
_____

What challenged me today? _____
_____
_____
_____
_____

How can I overcome that challenge? _____
_____
_____
_____
_____

What did I savor today? _____
_____
_____
_____

BUILDING *the* BEST YOU THERE IS

What did I do today? _____

_____

_____

_____

_____

What did I feel today? _____

_____

_____

_____

_____

What am I grateful for today? _____

_____

_____

_____

_____

What challenged me today? _____

_____

_____

_____

_____

How can I overcome that challenge? _____

_____

_____

_____

_____

What did I savor today? _____

_____

_____

_____

_____

What did I do today? _____

_____

_____

_____

_____

What did I feel today? _____

_____

_____

_____

_____

What am I grateful for today? _____

_____

_____

_____

_____

What challenged me today? _____

_____

_____

_____

_____

How can I overcome that challenge? _____

_____

_____

_____

_____

What did I savor today? _____

_____

_____

_____

_____

YEAR ONE

YEAR TWO

BUILDING *the* BEST YOU THERE IS

Date _____

What did I do today? _____
_____
_____
_____

What did I feel today? _____
_____
_____
_____

What am I grateful for today? _____
_____
_____
_____

What challenged me today? _____
_____
_____
_____

How can I overcome that challenge? _____
_____
_____
_____

What did I savor today? _____
_____
_____
_____

YEAR ONE

Date _____

What did I do today? _____
_____
_____
_____

What did I feel today? _____
_____
_____
_____

What am I grateful for today? _____
_____
_____
_____

What challenged me today? _____
_____
_____
_____

How can I overcome that challenge? _____
_____
_____
_____

What did I savor today? _____
_____
_____
_____

YEAR TWO

BUILDING *the* BEST YOU THERE IS

	_____ Date		_____ Date
What did I do today? _____		*What did I do today?* _____	

What did I do today? _____

_____

_____

_____

What did I feel today? _____

_____

_____

_____

What am I grateful for today? _____

_____

_____

_____

What challenged me today? _____

_____

_____

_____

How can I overcome that challenge? _____

_____

_____

_____

What did I savor today? _____

_____

_____

_____

What did I do today? _____

_____

_____

_____

What did I feel today? _____

_____

_____

_____

What am I grateful for today? _____

_____

_____

_____

What challenged me today? _____

_____

_____

_____

How can I overcome that challenge? _____

_____

_____

_____

What did I savor today? _____

_____

_____

_____

Year One   Year Two

BUILDING *the* BEST YOU THERE IS

	Date		Date

What did I do today? _____

_____

_____

_____

_____

What did I feel today? _____

_____

_____

_____

_____

What am I grateful for today? _____

_____

_____

_____

_____

What challenged me today? _____

_____

_____

_____

How can I overcome that challenge? _____

_____

_____

_____

_____

What did I savor today? _____

_____

_____

_____

_____

What did I do today? _____

_____

_____

_____

_____

What did I feel today? _____

_____

_____

_____

_____

What am I grateful for today? _____

_____

_____

_____

_____

What challenged me today? _____

_____

_____

_____

How can I overcome that challenge? _____

_____

_____

_____

_____

What did I savor today? _____

_____

_____

_____

_____

YEAR ONE

YEAR TWO

BUILDING *the* BEST YOU THERE IS

_____ Date

What did I do today? _____
_____
_____
_____
_____

What did I feel today? _____
_____
_____
_____
_____

What am I grateful for today? _____
_____
_____
_____
_____

What challenged me today? _____
_____
_____
_____
_____

How can I overcome that challenge? ____
_____
_____
_____
_____

What did I savor today? _____
_____
_____
_____
_____

YEAR ONE

_____ Date

What did I do today? _____
_____
_____
_____
_____

What did I feel today? _____
_____
_____
_____
_____

What am I grateful for today? _____
_____
_____
_____
_____

What challenged me today? _____
_____
_____
_____
_____

How can I overcome that challenge? ____
_____
_____
_____
_____

What did I savor today? _____
_____
_____
_____
_____

YEAR TWO

BUILDING _the_ BEST YOU THERE IS

Date

Date

What did I do today? _____

What did I do today? _____

_____

_____

_____

_____

_____

_____

What did I feel today? _____

What did I feel today? _____

_____

_____

_____

_____

_____

_____

What am I grateful for today? _____

What am I grateful for today? _____

_____

_____

_____

_____

_____

_____

_____

_____

What challenged me today? _____

What challenged me today? _____

_____

_____

_____

_____

_____

_____

_____

_____

How can I overcome that challenge? _____

How can I overcome that challenge? _____

_____

_____

_____

_____

_____

_____

_____

_____

What did I savor today? _____

What did I savor today? _____

_____

_____

_____

_____

_____

_____

YEAR ONE

YEAR TWO

BUILDING the BEST YOU THERE IS

_____ Date   _____ Date

What did I do today? _____   *What did I do today?* _____
_____   _____
_____   _____
_____   _____
_____   _____

What did I feel today? _____   *What did I feel today?* _____
_____   _____
_____   _____
_____   _____
_____   _____

What am I grateful for today? _____   *What am I grateful for today?* _____
_____   _____
_____   _____
_____   _____
_____   _____

What challenged me today? _____   *What challenged me today?* _____
_____   _____
_____   _____
_____   _____
_____   _____

How can I overcome that challenge? ___ *How can I overcome that challenge?* ___
_____   _____
_____   _____
_____   _____
_____   _____

What did I savor today? _____   *What did I savor today?* _____
_____   _____
_____   _____
_____   _____
_____   _____

BUILDING *the* BEST YOU THERE IS

_____ Date   _____ Date

What did I do today? _____   What did I do today? _____
_____   _____
_____   _____
_____   _____
_____   _____

What did I feel today? _____   What did I feel today? _____
_____   _____
_____   _____
_____   _____

What am I grateful for today? _____   What am I grateful for today? _____
_____   _____
_____   _____
_____   _____

What challenged me today? _____   What challenged me today? _____
_____   _____
_____   _____
_____   _____

How can I overcome that challenge? ___   How can I overcome that challenge? ___
_____   _____
_____   _____
_____   _____
_____   _____

What did I savor today? _____   What did I savor today? _____
_____   _____
_____   _____
_____   _____
_____   _____

YEAR ONE   YEAR TWO

BUILDING _the_ BEST YOU THERE IS

_____ Date   _____ Date

What did I do today? _____   What did I do today? _____
_____   _____
_____   _____
_____   _____

What did I feel today? _____   What did I feel today? _____
_____   _____
_____   _____
_____   _____

What am I grateful for today? _____   What am I grateful for today? _____
_____   _____
_____   _____
_____   _____

What challenged me today? _____   What challenged me today? _____
_____   _____
_____   _____
_____   _____

How can I overcome that challenge? ___   How can I overcome that challenge? ___
_____   _____
_____   _____
_____   _____

What did I savor today? _____   What did I savor today? _____
_____   _____
_____   _____
_____   _____

YEAR ONE   YEAR TWO

BUILDING *the* BEST YOU THERE IS

_____ Date

What did I do today? _____
_____
_____
_____

What did I feel today? _____
_____
_____
_____

What am I grateful for today? _____
_____
_____
_____

What challenged me today? _____
_____
_____
_____

How can I overcome that challenge? ___
_____
_____
_____

What did I savor today? _____
_____
_____
_____
_____

YEAR ONE

_____ Date

What did I do today? _____
_____
_____
_____

What did I feel today? _____
_____
_____
_____

What am I grateful for today? _____
_____
_____
_____

What challenged me today? _____
_____
_____
_____

How can I overcome that challenge? ___
_____
_____
_____

What did I savor today? _____
_____
_____
_____
_____

YEAR TWO

BUILDING _the_ BEST YOU THERE IS

_____ Date

What did I do today? _____
_____
_____
_____
_____

What did I feel today? _____
_____
_____
_____
_____

What am I grateful for today? _____
_____
_____
_____
_____

What challenged me today? _____
_____
_____
_____
_____

How can I overcome that challenge? _____
_____
_____
_____
_____

What did I savor today? _____
_____
_____
_____
_____

YEAR ONE

_____ Date

What did I do today? _____
_____
_____
_____
_____

What did I feel today? _____
_____
_____
_____
_____

What am I grateful for today? _____
_____
_____
_____
_____

What challenged me today? _____
_____
_____
_____
_____

How can I overcome that challenge? _____
_____
_____
_____
_____

What did I savor today? _____
_____
_____
_____
_____

YEAR TWO

BUILDING _the_ BEST YOU THERE IS

_____ Date   _____ Date

What did I do today? _____   *What did I do today?* _____
_____   _____
_____   _____
_____   _____
_____   _____

What did I feel today? _____   *What did I feel today?* _____
_____   _____
_____   _____
_____   _____
_____   _____

What am I grateful for today? _____   *What am I grateful for today?* _____
_____   _____
_____   _____
_____   _____
_____   _____

What challenged me today? _____   *What challenged me today?* _____
_____   _____
_____   _____
_____   _____
_____   _____

How can I overcome that challenge? _____   *How can I overcome that challenge?* _____
_____   _____
_____   _____
_____   _____
_____   _____

What did I savor today? _____   *What did I savor today?* _____
_____   _____
_____   _____
_____   _____
_____   _____

YEAR ONE   YEAR TWO

BUILDING *the* BEST YOU THERE IS

                                                    _____ Date   _____ Date

What did I do today? _____   *What did I do today?* _____
_____   _____
_____   _____
_____   _____
_____   _____

What did I feel today? _____   *What did I feel today?* _____
_____   _____
_____   _____
_____   _____
_____   _____

What am I grateful for today? _____   *What am I grateful for today?* _____
_____   _____
_____   _____
_____   _____
_____   _____

What challenged me today? _____   *What challenged me today?* _____
_____   _____
_____   _____
_____   _____
_____   _____

How can I overcome that challenge? ___   *How can I overcome that challenge?* ___
_____   _____
_____   _____
_____   _____
_____   _____

What did I savor today? _____   *What did I savor today?* _____
_____   _____
_____   _____
_____   _____
_____   _____

                                  YEAR ONE   YEAR TWO

BUILDING *the* BEST YOU THERE IS

_____ Date   _____ Date

What did I do today? _____   What did I do today? _____
_____   _____
_____   _____
_____   _____
_____   _____

What did I feel today? _____   What did I feel today? _____
_____   _____
_____   _____
_____   _____

What am I grateful for today? _____   What am I grateful for today? _____
_____   _____
_____   _____
_____   _____

What challenged me today? _____   What challenged me today? _____
_____   _____
_____   _____
_____   _____

How can I overcome that challenge? _____   How can I overcome that challenge? _____
_____   _____
_____   _____
_____   _____

What did I savor today? _____   What did I savor today? _____
_____   _____
_____   _____
_____   _____

YEAR ONE   YEAR TWO

BUILDING _the_ BEST YOU THERE IS

_____ Date   _____ Date

What did I do today? _____   _What did I do today?_ _____

_____   _____

_____   _____

_____   _____

_____   _____

What did I feel today? _____   _What did I feel today?_ _____

_____   _____

_____   _____

_____   _____

_____   _____

What am I grateful for today? _____   _What am I grateful for today?_ _____

_____   _____

_____   _____

_____   _____

_____   _____

What challenged me today? _____   _What challenged me today?_ _____

_____   _____

_____   _____

_____   _____

_____   _____

How can I overcome that challenge? _____   _How can I overcome that challenge?_ _____

_____   _____

_____   _____

_____   _____

_____   _____

What did I savor today? _____   _What did I savor today?_ _____

_____   _____

_____   _____

_____   _____

_____   _____

YEAR ONE   YEAR TWO

BUILDING _the_ BEST YOU THERE IS

What did I do today? _____   What did I do today? _____
_____   _____
_____   _____
_____   _____

What did I feel today? _____   What did I feel today? _____
_____   _____
_____   _____
_____   _____

What am I grateful for today? _____   What am I grateful for today? _____
_____   _____
_____   _____
_____   _____

What challenged me today? _____   What challenged me today? _____
_____   _____
_____   _____
_____   _____

How can I overcome that challenge? _____   How can I overcome that challenge? _____
_____   _____
_____   _____
_____   _____

What did I savor today? _____   What did I savor today? _____
_____   _____
_____   _____
_____   _____

_____ Date

What did I do today? _____

_____
_____
_____
_____

What did I feel today? _____

_____
_____
_____
_____

What am I grateful for today? _____

_____
_____
_____
_____

What challenged me today? _____

_____
_____
_____
_____

How can I overcome that challenge? _____

_____
_____
_____
_____

What did I savor today? _____

_____
_____
_____
_____

_____ Date

What did I do today? _____

_____
_____
_____
_____

What did I feel today? _____

_____
_____
_____
_____

What am I grateful for today? _____

_____
_____
_____
_____

What challenged me today? _____

_____
_____
_____
_____

How can I overcome that challenge? _____

_____
_____
_____
_____

What did I savor today? _____

_____
_____
_____
_____

YEAR TWO

BUILDING *the* BEST YOU THERE IS

_____ Date

What did I do today? _____
_____
_____
_____
_____

What did I feel today? _____
_____
_____
_____
_____

What am I grateful for today? _____
_____
_____
_____
_____

What challenged me today? _____
_____
_____
_____

How can I overcome that challenge? _____
_____
_____
_____
_____

What did I savor today? _____
_____
_____
_____
_____

YEAR ONE

_____ Date

What did I do today? _____
_____
_____
_____
_____

What did I feel today? _____
_____
_____
_____
_____

What am I grateful for today? _____
_____
_____
_____
_____

What challenged me today? _____
_____
_____
_____

How can I overcome that challenge? _____
_____
_____
_____
_____

What did I savor today? _____
_____
_____
_____
_____

YEAR TWO

BUILDING _the_ BEST YOU THERE IS

_____ Date

What did I do today? _____
_____
_____
_____
_____

What did I feel today? _____
_____
_____
_____
_____

What am I grateful for today? _____
_____
_____
_____
_____

What challenged me today? _____
_____
_____
_____
_____

How can I overcome that challenge? _____
_____
_____
_____
_____

What did I savor today? _____
_____
_____
_____
_____

YEAR ONE

_____ Date

What did I do today? _____
_____
_____
_____
_____

What did I feel today? _____
_____
_____
_____
_____

What am I grateful for today? _____
_____
_____
_____
_____

What challenged me today? _____
_____
_____
_____
_____

How can I overcome that challenge? _____
_____
_____
_____
_____

What did I savor today? _____
_____
_____
_____
_____

YEAR TWO

BUILDING _the_ BEST YOU THERE IS

_____ Date

What did I do today? _____
_____
_____
_____

What did I feel today? _____
_____
_____
_____

What am I grateful for today? _____
_____
_____
_____

What challenged me today? _____
_____
_____
_____

How can I overcome that challenge? _____
_____
_____
_____

What did I savor today? _____
_____
_____
_____

_____ Date

What did I do today? _____
_____
_____
_____

What did I feel today? _____
_____
_____
_____

What am I grateful for today? _____
_____
_____
_____

What challenged me today? _____
_____
_____
_____

How can I overcome that challenge? _____
_____
_____
_____

What did I savor today? _____
_____
_____
_____

BUILDING _the_ BEST YOU THERE IS

What do I value most in life? _____
_____
_____
_____
_____

Am I influenced by material things? _____
_____
_____
_____
_____

Do I treasure family? _____
_____
_____
_____
_____

What do I admire most about others? _____
_____
_____
_____
_____

How do I picture myself in twenty years? _____
_____
_____
_____
_____

How do I get there? _____
_____
_____
_____
_____

BUILDING *the* BEST YOU THERE IS

Am I bound to the past? _____

_____
_____
_____
_____

Do I repeat old patterns? _____

_____
_____
_____
_____

Do I long for a new direction? _____

_____
_____
_____
_____

What is that direction? _____

_____
_____
_____
_____

How do I get there? _____

_____
_____
_____
_____

What's my first step to take? _____

_____
_____
_____
_____

What do I value most in life? _____

_____

_____

_____

_____

Am I influenced by material things? _____

_____

_____

_____

_____

Do I treasure family? _____

_____

_____

_____

_____

What do I admire most about others? _____

_____

_____

_____

_____

How do I picture myself in twenty years? _____

_____

_____

_____

_____

How do I get there? _____

_____

_____

_____

_____

Am I bound to the past? _____

_____
_____
_____
_____

Do I repeat old patterns? _____

_____
_____
_____
_____

Do I long for a new direction? _____

_____
_____
_____
_____

What is that direction? _____

_____
_____
_____
_____

How do I get there? _____

_____
_____
_____
_____

What's my first step to take? _____

_____
_____
_____
_____

_____ Date | _____ Date

What did I do today? _____

_____

_____

_____

_____

What did I feel today? _____

_____

_____

_____

_____

What am I grateful for today? _____

_____

_____

_____

_____

What challenged me today? _____

_____

_____

_____

_____

How can I overcome that challenge? _____

_____

_____

_____

_____

What did I savor today? _____

_____

_____

_____

_____

What did I do today? _____

_____

_____

_____

_____

What did I feel today? _____

_____

_____

_____

_____

What am I grateful for today? _____

_____

_____

_____

_____

What challenged me today? _____

_____

_____

_____

_____

How can I overcome that challenge? _____

_____

_____

_____

_____

What did I savor today? _____

_____

_____

_____

_____

YEAR ONE   YEAR TWO

BUILDING _the_ BEST YOU THERE IS

What did I do today? _____
_____
_____
_____
_____

What did I feel today? _____
_____
_____
_____
_____

What am I grateful for today? _____
_____
_____
_____
_____

What challenged me today? _____
_____
_____
_____
_____

How can I overcome that challenge? _____
_____
_____
_____
_____

What did I savor today? _____
_____
_____
_____
_____

What did I do today? _____
_____
_____
_____
_____

What did I feel today? _____
_____
_____
_____
_____

What am I grateful for today? _____
_____
_____
_____
_____

What challenged me today? _____
_____
_____
_____
_____

How can I overcome that challenge? _____
_____
_____
_____
_____

What did I savor today? _____
_____
_____
_____
_____

BUILDING *the* BEST YOU THERE IS

_____ Date

What did I do today? _____

_____
_____
_____
_____

What did I feel today? _____

_____
_____
_____
_____

What am I grateful for today? _____

_____
_____
_____
_____

What challenged me today? _____

_____
_____
_____
_____

How can I overcome that challenge? _____

_____
_____
_____
_____

What did I savor today? _____

_____
_____
_____
_____

YEAR ONE

_____ Date

What did I do today? _____

_____
_____
_____
_____

What did I feel today? _____

_____
_____
_____
_____

What am I grateful for today? _____

_____
_____
_____
_____

What challenged me today? _____

_____
_____
_____
_____

How can I overcome that challenge? _____

_____
_____
_____
_____

What did I savor today? _____

_____
_____
_____
_____

YEAR TWO

BUILDING _the_ BEST YOU THERE IS

_____ Date

What did I do today? _____
_____
_____
_____
_____

What did I feel today? _____
_____
_____
_____

What am I grateful for today? _____
_____
_____
_____

What challenged me today? _____
_____
_____
_____

How can I overcome that challenge? _____
_____
_____
_____

What did I savor today? _____
_____
_____
_____

YEAR ONE

_____ Date

What did I do today? _____
_____
_____
_____
_____

What did I feel today? _____
_____
_____
_____

What am I grateful for today? _____
_____
_____
_____

What challenged me today? _____
_____
_____
_____

How can I overcome that challenge? _____
_____
_____
_____

What did I savor today? _____
_____
_____
_____

YEAR TWO

BUILDING the BEST YOU THERE IS

What did I do today? _____

What did I do today? _____

_____

_____

_____

_____

_____

_____

What did I feel today? _____

What did I feel today? _____

_____

_____

_____

_____

_____

_____

What am I grateful for today? _____

What am I grateful for today? _____

_____

_____

_____

_____

_____

_____

What challenged me today? _____

What challenged me today? _____

_____

_____

_____

_____

_____

_____

How can I overcome that challenge? _____

How can I overcome that challenge? _____

_____

_____

_____

_____

_____

_____

What did I savor today? _____

What did I savor today? _____

_____

_____

_____

_____

_____

_____

BUILDING *the* BEST YOU THERE IS

What did I do today? _____

_____

_____

_____

_____

What did I feel today? _____

_____

_____

_____

_____

What am I grateful for today? _____

_____

_____

_____

_____

What challenged me today? _____

_____

_____

_____

_____

How can I overcome that challenge? _____

_____

_____

_____

_____

What did I savor today? _____

_____

_____

_____

_____

———————— *Date*

What did I do today? _____

_____

_____

_____

_____

What did I feel today? _____

_____

_____

_____

_____

What am I grateful for today? _____

_____

_____

_____

_____

What challenged me today? _____

_____

_____

_____

_____

How can I overcome that challenge? _____

_____

_____

_____

_____

What did I savor today? _____

_____

_____

_____

_____

YEAR ONE   YEAR TWO

BUILDING *the* BEST YOU THERE IS

_____ Date

_____ Date

What did I do today? _____

What did I do today? _____

_____
_____
_____
_____

_____
_____
_____
_____

What did I feel today? _____

What did I feel today? _____

_____
_____
_____
_____

_____
_____
_____
_____

What am I grateful for today? _____

What am I grateful for today? _____

_____
_____
_____
_____

_____
_____
_____
_____

What challenged me today? _____

What challenged me today? _____

_____
_____
_____
_____

_____
_____
_____
_____

How can I overcome that challenge? _____

How can I overcome that challenge? _____

_____
_____
_____
_____

_____
_____
_____
_____

What did I savor today? _____

What did I savor today? _____

_____
_____
_____
_____

_____
_____
_____
_____

YEAR ONE

YEAR TWO

BUILDING *the* BEST YOU THERE IS

What did I do today? _____

_____

_____

_____

What did I feel today? _____

_____

_____

_____

What am I grateful for today? _____

_____

_____

_____

What challenged me today? _____

_____

_____

_____

How can I overcome that challenge? _____

_____

_____

_____

What did I savor today? _____

_____

_____

_____

YEAR ONE

Date _____

What did I do today? _____

_____

_____

_____

What did I feel today? _____

_____

_____

_____

What am I grateful for today? _____

_____

_____

_____

What challenged me today? _____

_____

_____

_____

How can I overcome that challenge? _____

_____

_____

_____

What did I savor today? _____

_____

_____

_____

YEAR TWO

_____ Date

What did I do today? _____
_____
_____
_____
_____

What did I feel today? _____
_____
_____
_____
_____

What am I grateful for today? _____
_____
_____
_____
_____

What challenged me today? _____
_____
_____
_____
_____

How can I overcome that challenge? _____
_____
_____
_____
_____

What did I savor today? _____
_____
_____
_____
_____

YEAR ONE

_____ Date

What did I do today? _____
_____
_____
_____
_____

What did I feel today? _____
_____
_____
_____
_____

What am I grateful for today? _____
_____
_____
_____
_____

What challenged me today? _____
_____
_____
_____
_____

How can I overcome that challenge? _____
_____
_____
_____
_____

What did I savor today? _____
_____
_____
_____
_____

YEAR TWO

BUILDING _the_ BEST YOU THERE IS

_____ Date

What did I do today? _____

_____

_____

_____

_____

What did I feel today? _____

_____

_____

_____

_____

What am I grateful for today? _____

_____

_____

_____

_____

What challenged me today? _____

_____

_____

_____

_____

How can I overcome that challenge? _____

_____

_____

_____

_____

What did I savor today? _____

_____

_____

_____

_____

YEAR ONE

_____ Date

What did I do today? _____

_____

_____

_____

_____

What did I feel today? _____

_____

_____

_____

_____

What am I grateful for today? _____

_____

_____

_____

_____

What challenged me today? _____

_____

_____

_____

_____

How can I overcome that challenge? _____

_____

_____

_____

_____

What did I savor today? _____

_____

_____

_____

_____

YEAR TWO

BUILDING _the_ BEST YOU THERE IS

_____ Date   _____ Date

What did I do today? _____   What did I do today? _____
_____   _____
_____   _____
_____   _____

What did I feel today? _____   What did I feel today? _____
_____   _____
_____   _____
_____   _____

What am I grateful for today? _____   What am I grateful for today? _____
_____   _____
_____   _____
_____   _____

What challenged me today? _____   What challenged me today? _____
_____   _____
_____   _____
_____   _____

How can I overcome that challenge? _____   How can I overcome that challenge? _____
_____   _____
_____   _____
_____   _____

What did I savor today? _____   What did I savor today? _____
_____   _____
_____   _____
_____   _____

YEAR ONE   YEAR TWO

BUILDING *the* BEST YOU THERE IS

_____ Date   _____ Date

What did I do today? _____   What did I do today? _____
_____   _____
_____   _____
_____   _____

What did I feel today? _____   What did I feel today? _____
_____   _____
_____   _____
_____   _____

What am I grateful for today? _____   What am I grateful for today? _____
_____   _____
_____   _____
_____   _____

What challenged me today? _____   What challenged me today? _____
_____   _____
_____   _____
_____   _____

How can I overcome that challenge? ____   How can I overcome that challenge? ____
_____   _____
_____   _____
_____   _____

What did I savor today? _____   What did I savor today? _____
_____   _____
_____   _____
_____   _____

YEAR ONE   YEAR TWO

BUILDING _the_ BEST YOU THERE IS

_____ Date

What did I do today? _____
_____
_____
_____
_____

What did I feel today? _____
_____
_____
_____
_____

What am I grateful for today? _____
_____
_____
_____
_____

What challenged me today? _____
_____
_____
_____
_____

How can I overcome that challenge? _____
_____
_____
_____
_____

What did I savor today? _____
_____
_____
_____
_____

YEAR ONE

_____ Date

What did I do today? _____
_____
_____
_____
_____

What did I feel today? _____
_____
_____
_____
_____

What am I grateful for today? _____
_____
_____
_____
_____

What challenged me today? _____
_____
_____
_____
_____

How can I overcome that challenge? _____
_____
_____
_____
_____

What did I savor today? _____
_____
_____
_____
_____

YEAR TWO

BUILDING _the_ BEST YOU THERE IS

What did I do today? _____

_____
_____
_____

What did I feel today? _____

_____
_____
_____

What am I grateful for today? _____ __

_____
_____
_____
_____

What challenged me today? _____

_____
_____
_____

How can I overcome that challenge? _____

_____
_____
_____

What did I savor today? _____

_____
_____
_____

What did I do today? _____

_____
_____
_____

What did I feel today? _____

_____
_____
_____

What am I grateful for today? _____

_____
_____
_____
_____

What challenged me today? _____

_____
_____
_____

How can I overcome that challenge? _____

_____
_____
_____

What did I savor today? _____

_____
_____
_____

YEAR ONE

YEAR TWO

BUILDING the BEST YOU THERE IS

Date _____

What did I do today? _____
_____
_____
_____
_____

What did I feel today? _____
_____
_____
_____
_____

What am I grateful for today? _____
_____
_____
_____
_____

What challenged me today? _____
_____
_____
_____
_____

How can I overcome that challenge? _____
_____
_____
_____
_____

What did I savor today? _____
_____
_____
_____
_____

YEAR ONE

Date _____

What did I do today? _____
_____
_____
_____
_____

What did I feel today? _____
_____
_____
_____
_____

What am I grateful for today? _____
_____
_____
_____
_____

What challenged me today? _____
_____
_____
_____
_____

How can I overcome that challenge? _____
_____
_____
_____
_____

What did I savor today? _____
_____
_____
_____
_____

YEAR TWO

BUILDING the BEST YOU THERE IS

_____ Date

What did I do today? _____
_____
_____
_____

What did I feel today? _____
_____
_____
_____

What am I grateful for today? _____
_____
_____
_____

What challenged me today? _____
_____
_____
_____

How can I overcome that challenge? _____
_____
_____
_____

What did I savor today? _____
_____
_____
_____

YEAR ONE

_____ Date

What did I do today? _____
_____
_____
_____

What did I feel today? _____
_____
_____
_____

What am I grateful for today? _____
_____
_____
_____

What challenged me today? _____
_____
_____
_____

How can I overcome that challenge? _____
_____
_____
_____

What did I savor today? _____
_____
_____
_____

YEAR TWO

BUILDING _the_ BEST YOU THERE IS

_____ Date

What did I do today? _____
_____
_____
_____
_____

What did I feel today? _____
_____
_____
_____
_____

What am I grateful for today? _____
_____
_____
_____
_____

What challenged me today? _____
_____
_____
_____
_____

How can I overcome that challenge? ___
_____
_____
_____
_____

What did I savor today? _____
_____
_____
_____

YEAR ONE

_____ Date

What did I do today? _____
_____
_____
_____
_____

What did I feel today? _____
_____
_____
_____
_____

What am I grateful for today? _____
_____
_____
_____
_____

What challenged me today? _____
_____
_____
_____
_____

How can I overcome that challenge? ___
_____
_____
_____
_____

What did I savor today? _____
_____
_____
_____

YEAR TWO

BUILDING *the* BEST YOU THERE IS

_____ Date

What did I do today? _____

_____

_____

_____

What did I feel today? _____

_____

_____

_____

What am I grateful for today? _____

_____

_____

_____

What challenged me today? _____

_____

_____

_____

How can I overcome that challenge? _____

_____

_____

_____

What did I savor today? _____

_____

_____

_____

YEAR ONE

_____ Date

What did I do today? _____

_____

_____

_____

What did I feel today? _____

_____

_____

_____

What am I grateful for today? _____

_____

_____

_____

What challenged me today? _____

_____

_____

_____

How can I overcome that challenge? _____

_____

_____

_____

What did I savor today? _____

_____

_____

_____

YEAR TWO

BUILDING _the_ BEST YOU THERE IS

_____ Date   _____ Date

What did I do today? _____   What did I do today? _____
_____   _____
_____   _____
_____   _____
_____   _____

What did I feel today? _____   What did I feel today? _____
_____   _____
_____   _____
_____   _____
_____   _____

What am I grateful for today? _____   What am I grateful for today? _____
_____   _____
_____   _____
_____   _____
_____   _____

What challenged me today? _____   What challenged me today? _____
_____   _____
_____   _____
_____   _____
_____   _____

How can I overcome that challenge? ___   How can I overcome that challenge? ___
_____   _____
_____   _____
_____   _____
_____   _____

What did I savor today? _____   What did I savor today? _____
_____   _____
_____   _____
_____   _____
_____   _____

YEAR ONE   YEAR TWO

BUILDING _the_ BEST YOU THERE IS

_____ Date

What did I do today? _____

_____

_____

_____

_____

What did I feel today? _____

_____

_____

_____

_____

What am I grateful for today? _____

_____

_____

_____

_____

What challenged me today? _____

_____

_____

_____

_____

How can I overcome that challenge? _____

_____

_____

_____

_____

What did I savor today? _____

_____

_____

_____

_____

YEAR ONE

_____ Date

What did I do today? _____

_____

_____

_____

_____

What did I feel today? _____

_____

_____

_____

_____

What am I grateful for today? _____

_____

_____

_____

_____

What challenged me today? _____

_____

_____

_____

_____

How can I overcome that challenge? _____

_____

_____

_____

_____

What did I savor today? _____

_____

_____

_____

_____

YEAR TWO

BUILDING the BEST YOU THERE IS

_____ Date

What did I do today? _____
_____
_____
_____
_____

What did I feel today? _____
_____
_____
_____
_____

What am I grateful for today? _____
_____
_____
_____

What challenged me today? _____
_____
_____
_____

How can I overcome that challenge? _____
_____
_____
_____

What did I savor today? _____
_____
_____
_____

_____ Date

What did I do today? _____
_____
_____
_____
_____

What did I feel today? _____
_____
_____
_____
_____

What am I grateful for today? _____
_____
_____
_____

What challenged me today? _____
_____
_____
_____

How can I overcome that challenge? _____
_____
_____
_____

What did I savor today? _____
_____
_____
_____

YEAR ONE

YEAR TWO

BUILDING *the* BEST YOU THERE IS

_____ Date   _____ Date

What did I do today? _____   What did I do today? _____
_____   _____
_____   _____
_____   _____
_____   _____

What did I feel today? _____ What did I feel today? _____
_____   _____
_____   _____
_____   _____
_____   _____

What am I grateful for today? _____   What am I grateful for today? _____
_____   _____
_____   _____
_____   _____
_____   _____

What challenged me today? _____   What challenged me today? _____
_____   _____
_____   _____
_____   _____

How can I overcome that challenge? ____ How can I overcome that challenge? ____
_____   _____
_____   _____
_____   _____

What did I savor today? _____   What did I savor today? _____
_____   _____
_____   _____
_____   _____

YEAR ONE   YEAR TWO

BUILDING *the* BEST YOU THERE IS

What did I do today? _____   Date

What did I do today? _____   Date

_____

_____

_____

_____

What did I feel today? _____

What did I feel today? _____

_____

_____

_____

_____

What am I grateful for today? _____

What am I grateful for today? _____

_____

_____

_____

_____

What challenged me today? _____

What challenged me today? _____

_____

_____

_____

_____

How can I overcome that challenge? _____

How can I overcome that challenge? _____

_____

_____

_____

_____

What did I savor today? _____

What did I savor today? _____

_____

_____

_____

_____

YEAR ONE

YEAR TWO

BUILDING *the* BEST YOU THERE IS

What did I do today? _____

_____

_____

_____

_____

What did I feel today? _____

_____

_____

_____

What am I grateful for today? _____

_____

_____

_____

What challenged me today? _____

_____

_____

_____

How can I overcome that challenge? _____

_____

_____

_____

What did I savor today? _____

_____

_____

_____

What did I do today? _____

_____

_____

_____

_____

What did I feel today? _____

_____

_____

_____

What am I grateful for today? _____

_____

_____

_____

What challenged me today? _____

_____

_____

_____

How can I overcome that challenge? _____

_____

_____

_____

What did I savor today? _____

_____

_____

_____

YEAR ONE   YEAR TWO

BUILDING *the* BEST YOU THERE IS

_____ Date

What did I do today? _____
_____
_____
_____
_____

What did I feel today? _____
_____
_____
_____
_____

What am I grateful for today? _____
_____
_____
_____
_____

What challenged me today? _____
_____
_____
_____
_____

How can I overcome that challenge? _____
_____
_____
_____
_____

What did I savor today? _____
_____
_____
_____
_____

YEAR ONE

_____ Date

What did I do today? _____
_____
_____
_____
_____

What did I feel today? _____
_____
_____
_____
_____

What am I grateful for today? _____
_____
_____
_____
_____

What challenged me today? _____
_____
_____
_____
_____

How can I overcome that challenge? _____
_____
_____
_____
_____

What did I savor today? _____
_____
_____
_____
_____

YEAR TWO

BUILDING *the* BEST YOU THERE IS

_____ Date   _____ Date

What did I do today? _____   *What did I do today?* _____

_____   _____

_____   _____

_____   _____

_____   _____

What did I feel today? _____   *What did I feel today?* _____

_____   _____

_____   _____

_____   _____

_____   _____

What am I grateful for today? _____   *What am I grateful for today?* _____

_____   _____

_____   _____

_____   _____

What challenged me today? _____   *What challenged me today?* _____

_____   _____

_____   _____

_____   _____

How can I overcome that challenge? _____   *How can I overcome that challenge?* _____

_____   _____

_____   _____

_____   _____

What did I savor today? _____   *What did I savor today?* _____

_____   _____

_____   _____

_____   _____

YEAR ONE   YEAR TWO

BUILDING *the* BEST YOU THERE IS

_____ Date

What did I do today? _____
_____
_____
_____

What did I feel today? _____
_____
_____
_____

What am I grateful for today? _____
_____
_____
_____

What challenged me today? _____
_____
_____
_____

How can I overcome that challenge? _____
_____
_____
_____

What did I savor today? _____
_____
_____
_____

_____ Date

What did I do today? _____
_____
_____
_____

What did I feel today? _____
_____
_____
_____

What am I grateful for today? _____
_____
_____
_____

What challenged me today? _____
_____
_____
_____

How can I overcome that challenge? _____
_____
_____
_____

What did I savor today? _____
_____
_____
_____

Date _____	*Date* _____
What did I do today? _____	What did I do today? _____
_____	_____
_____	_____
_____	_____
What did I feel today? _____	What did I feel today? _____
_____	_____
_____	_____
_____	_____
What am I grateful for today? _____	What am I grateful for today? _____
_____	_____
_____	_____
_____	_____
What challenged me today? _____	What challenged me today? _____
_____	_____
_____	_____
_____	_____
How can I overcome that challenge? _____	How can I overcome that challenge? _____
_____	_____
_____	_____
_____	_____
What did I savor today? _____	What did I savor today? _____
_____	_____
_____	_____
_____	_____
YEAR ONE	YEAR TWO

BUILDING *the* BEST YOU THERE IS

_____ Date

What did I do today? _____

_____

_____

_____

_____

What did I feel today? _____

_____

_____

_____

_____

What am I grateful for today? _____

_____

_____

_____

_____

What challenged me today? _____

_____

_____

_____

_____

How can I overcome that challenge? _____

_____

_____

_____

_____

What did I savor today? _____

_____

_____

_____

_____

YEAR ONE

_____ Date

What did I do today? _____

_____

_____

_____

_____

What did I feel today? _____

_____

_____

_____

_____

What am I grateful for today? _____

_____

_____

_____

_____

What challenged me today? _____

_____

_____

_____

_____

How can I overcome that challenge? _____

_____

_____

_____

_____

What did I savor today? _____

_____

_____

_____

_____

YEAR TWO

BUILDING *the* BEST YOU THERE IS

_____ Date   _____ Date

What did I do today? _____   *What did I do today?* _____
_____   _____
_____   _____
_____   _____
_____   _____

What did I feel today? _____   *What did I feel today?* _____
_____   _____
_____   _____
_____   _____
_____   _____

What am I grateful for today? _____   *What am I grateful for today?* _____
_____   _____
_____   _____
_____   _____
_____   _____

What challenged me today? _____   *What challenged me today?* _____
_____   _____
_____   _____
_____   _____
_____   _____

How can I overcome that challenge? ___   *How can I overcome that challenge?* ___
_____   _____
_____   _____
_____   _____
_____   _____

What did I savor today? _____   *What did I savor today?* _____
_____   _____
_____   _____
_____   _____
_____   _____

YEAR ONE   YEAR TWO

BUILDING *the* BEST YOU THERE IS

_____ Date

What did I do today? _____
_____
_____
_____

What did I feel today? _____
_____
_____
_____

What am I grateful for today? _____
_____
_____
_____

What challenged me today? _____
_____
_____
_____

How can I overcome that challenge? _____
_____
_____
_____

What did I savor today? _____
_____
_____
_____

YEAR ONE

_____ Date

What did I do today? _____
_____
_____
_____

What did I feel today? _____
_____
_____
_____

What am I grateful for today? _____
_____
_____
_____

What challenged me today? _____
_____
_____
_____

How can I overcome that challenge? _____
_____
_____
_____

What did I savor today? _____
_____
_____
_____

YEAR TWO

BUILDING *the* BEST YOU THERE IS

_____ Date

What did I do today? _____
_____
_____
_____
_____

What did I feel today? _____
_____
_____
_____
_____

What am I grateful for today? _____
_____
_____
_____
_____

What challenged me today? _____
_____
_____
_____
_____

How can I overcome that challenge? _____
_____
_____
_____
_____

What did I savor today? _____
_____
_____
_____
_____

YEAR ONE

_____ Date

What did I do today? _____
_____
_____
_____
_____

What did I feel today? _____
_____
_____
_____
_____

What am I grateful for today? _____
_____
_____
_____
_____

What challenged me today? _____
_____
_____
_____
_____

How can I overcome that challenge? _____
_____
_____
_____
_____

What did I savor today? _____
_____
_____
_____
_____

YEAR TWO

_____ Date

What did I do today? _____
_____
_____
_____
_____

What did I feel today? _____
_____
_____
_____
_____

What am I grateful for today? _____
_____
_____
_____
_____

What challenged me today? _____
_____
_____
_____
_____

How can I overcome that challenge? _____
_____
_____
_____
_____

What did I savor today? _____
_____
_____
_____
_____

YEAR ONE

_____ Date

What did I do today? _____
_____
_____
_____
_____

What did I feel today? _____
_____
_____
_____
_____

What am I grateful for today? _____
_____
_____
_____
_____

What challenged me today? _____
_____
_____
_____
_____

How can I overcome that challenge? _____
_____
_____
_____
_____

What did I savor today? _____
_____
_____
_____
_____

YEAR TWO

BUILDING *the* BEST YOU THERE IS

_____ Date

What did I do today? _____
_____
_____
_____
_____

What did I feel today? _____
_____
_____
_____
_____

What am I grateful for today? _____
_____
_____
_____
_____

What challenged me today? _____
_____
_____
_____
_____

How can I overcome that challenge? _____
_____
_____
_____
_____

What did I savor today? _____
_____
_____
_____
_____

YEAR ONE

_____ Date

What did I do today? _____
_____
_____
_____
_____

What did I feel today? _____
_____
_____
_____
_____

What am I grateful for today? _____
_____
_____
_____
_____

What challenged me today? _____
_____
_____
_____
_____

How can I overcome that challenge? _____
_____
_____
_____
_____

What did I savor today? _____
_____
_____
_____
_____

YEAR TWO

BUILDING the BEST YOU THERE IS

_____ Date

What did I do today? _____
_____
_____
_____

What did I feel today? _____
_____
_____
_____

What am I grateful for today? _____
_____
_____
_____

What challenged me today? _____
_____
_____
_____

How can I overcome that challenge? _____
_____
_____
_____

What did I savor today? _____
_____
_____
_____

YEAR ONE

_____ Date

What did I do today? _____
_____
_____
_____

What did I feel today? _____
_____
_____
_____

What am I grateful for today? _____
_____
_____
_____

What challenged me today? _____
_____
_____
_____

How can I overcome that challenge? _____
_____
_____
_____

What did I savor today? _____
_____
_____
_____

YEAR TWO

BUILDING the BEST YOU THERE IS

_____ Date

What did I do today? _____

_____

_____

_____

What did I feel today? _____

_____

_____

_____

What am I grateful for today? _____

_____

_____

_____

What challenged me today? _____

_____

_____

_____

How can I overcome that challenge? _____

_____

_____

_____

What did I savor today? _____

_____

_____

_____

_____ Date

What did I do today? _____

_____

_____

_____

What did I feel today? _____

_____

_____

_____

What am I grateful for today? _____

_____

_____

_____

What challenged me today? _____

_____

_____

_____

How can I overcome that challenge? _____

_____

_____

_____

What did I savor today? _____

_____

_____

_____

BUILDING the BEST YOU THERE IS

_____ Date   _____ Date

What did I do today? _____   *What did I do today?* _____
_____   _____
_____   _____
_____   _____
_____   _____

What did I feel today? _____   *What did I feel today?* _____
_____   _____
_____   _____
_____   _____
_____   _____

What am I grateful for today? _____   *What am I grateful for today?* _____
_____   _____
_____   _____
_____   _____
_____   _____

What challenged me today? _____   *What challenged me today?* _____
_____   _____
_____   _____
_____   _____
_____   _____

How can I overcome that challenge? ___ *How can I overcome that challenge?* ___
_____   _____
_____   _____
_____   _____
_____   _____

What did I savor today? _____   *What did I savor today?* _____
_____   _____
_____   _____
_____   _____
_____   _____

YEAR ONE   YEAR TWO

BUILDING *the* BEST YOU THERE IS

What did I do today? _____

What did I do today? _____

_____

_____

_____

_____

_____

_____

What did I feel today? _____

What did I feel today? _____

_____

_____

_____

_____

_____

_____

What am I grateful for today? _____

What am I grateful for today? _____

_____

_____

_____

_____

_____

_____

What challenged me today? _____

What challenged me today? _____

_____

_____

_____

_____

_____

_____

_____

_____

How can I overcome that challenge? ____

How can I overcome that challenge? ____

_____

_____

_____

_____

_____

_____

What did I savor today? _____

What did I savor today? _____

_____

_____

_____

_____

_____

_____

YEAR ONE

YEAR TWO

BUILDING *the* BEST YOU THERE IS

_____ Date

What did I do today? _____
_____
_____
_____
_____

What did I feel today? _____
_____
_____
_____
_____

What am I grateful for today? _____
_____
_____
_____
_____

What challenged me today? _____
_____
_____
_____
_____

How can I overcome that challenge? _____
_____
_____
_____
_____

What did I savor today? _____
_____
_____
_____
_____

YEAR ONE

_____ Date

What did I do today? _____
_____
_____
_____
_____

What did I feel today? _____
_____
_____
_____
_____

What am I grateful for today? _____
_____
_____
_____
_____

What challenged me today? _____
_____
_____
_____
_____

How can I overcome that challenge? _____
_____
_____
_____
_____

What did I savor today? _____
_____
_____
_____
_____

YEAR TWO

BUILDING *the* BEST YOU THERE IS

_____ Date   _____ Date

What did I do today? _____   *What did I do today?* _____
_____   _____
_____   _____
_____   _____
_____   _____

What did I feel today? _____   *What did I feel today?* _____
_____   _____
_____   _____
_____   _____
_____   _____

What am I grateful for today? _____ *What am I grateful for today?* _____
_____   _____
_____   _____
_____   _____
_____   _____

What challenged me today? _____   *What challenged me today?* _____
_____   _____
_____   _____
_____   _____
_____   _____

How can I overcome that challenge? ___ *How can I overcome that challenge?* ___
_____   _____
_____   _____
_____   _____
_____   _____

What did I savor today? _____ *What did I savor today?* _____
_____   _____
_____   _____
_____   _____
_____   _____

YEAR ONE   YEAR TWO

BUILDING *the* BEST YOU THERE IS

_____ Date

What did I do today? _____
_____
_____
_____
_____

What did I feel today? _____
_____
_____
_____
_____

What am I grateful for today? _____
_____
_____
_____
_____

What challenged me today? _____
_____
_____
_____
_____

How can I overcome that challenge? _____
_____
_____
_____
_____

What did I savor today? _____
_____
_____
_____
_____

YEAR ONE

_____ Date

What did I do today? _____
_____
_____
_____
_____

What did I feel today? _____
_____
_____
_____
_____

What am I grateful for today? _____
_____
_____
_____
_____

What challenged me today? _____
_____
_____
_____
_____

How can I overcome that challenge? _____
_____
_____
_____
_____

What did I savor today? _____
_____
_____
_____
_____

YEAR TWO

BUILDING _the_ BEST YOU THERE IS

What did I do today? _____

_____

_____

_____

_____

What did I feel today? _____

_____

_____

_____

_____

What am I grateful for today? _____

_____

_____

_____

_____

What challenged me today? _____

_____

_____

_____

_____

How can I overcome that challenge? _____

_____

_____

_____

_____

What did I savor today? _____

_____

_____

_____

_____

YEAR ONE

What did I do today? _____

_____

_____

_____

_____

What did I feel today? _____

_____

_____

_____

_____

What am I grateful for today? _____

_____

_____

_____

_____

What challenged me today? _____

_____

_____

_____

_____

How can I overcome that challenge? _____

_____

_____

_____

_____

What did I savor today? _____

_____

_____

_____

_____

YEAR TWO

What do I think of myself? _____

_____

_____

_____

_____

What do other people think of me? _____

_____

_____

_____

_____

Do I present my true self to others? _____

_____

_____

_____

_____

Do I show others that I care? _____

_____

_____

_____

_____

Do I listen to others? _____

_____

_____

_____

_____

How can I be more tuned in? _____

_____

_____

_____

_____

BUILDING *the* BEST YOU THERE IS

Do I enjoy getting up in the morning? _____

_____

_____

_____

_____

Do I relish what I do? _____

_____

_____

_____

_____

Do I look forward to life? _____

_____

_____

_____

_____

What would resonate more with me? _____

_____

_____

_____

_____

Do I see the road to fulfillment? _____

_____

_____

_____

_____

How do I take that path? _____

_____

_____

_____

_____

What do I think of myself? _____

_____

_____

_____

_____

What do other people think of me? _____

_____

_____

_____

_____

Do I present my true self to others? _____

_____

_____

_____

_____

Do I show others that I care? _____

_____

_____

_____

_____

Do I listen to others? _____

_____

_____

_____

_____

How can I be more tuned in? _____

_____

_____

_____

_____

TWO

Do I enjoy getting up in the morning? _____
_____
_____
_____
_____

Do I relish what I do? _____
_____
_____
_____
_____

Do I look forward to life? _____
_____
_____
_____

What would resonate more with me? _____
_____
_____
_____
_____

Do I see the road to fulfillment? _____
_____
_____
_____

How do I take that path? _____
_____
_____
_____
_____